D1253299

The Smithsonian Institution

PRAEGER LIBRARY OF U.S. GOVERNMENT DEPARTMENTS
AND AGENCIES

Consulting Editors

ERNEST S. GRIFFITH

Former University Professor and Dean Emeritus, School of International Service, American University; former Director, Legislative Reference Service, Library of Congress; and author of *The American System of Government* and *The Modern Government in Action*

HUGH LANGDON ELSBREE

Former Chairman, Department of Political Science, Dartmouth College; former Managing Editor, *American Political Science Review*; former Director, Legislative Reference Service, Library of Congress

The Smithsonian Institution

Paul H. Oehser

PRAEGER PUBLISHERS

New York • Washington • London

For Grace, Gordon, Richard, Tina, Donnie, Tommy, and John Paul Jones, in the order of their appearance

---

PRAEGER PUBLISHERS
111 Fourth Avenue, New York, N.Y. 10003, U.S.A.
5, Cromwell Place, London S.W.7, England

Published in the United States of America in 1970
by Praeger Publishers, Inc.

Library of Congress Catalog Card Number: 74–95682

This book is No. 21 in the series
Praeger Library of U.S. Government Departments and Agencies

Printed in the United States of America

Foreword

S. Dillon Ripley
Secretary of the Smithsonian Institution

These are excited times. Extraordinary events occur in an arena of massive popularity: Social upheavals, geopolitical disasters, scientific spectaculars, and behavioral revolutions proceed concurrently. Here, and elsewhere, the middle-aged are out of touch with the young. From the turn of the century, the United States of America has sought, logically enough and by effective means, to prolong the *status quo*. The successes of conservatism have reaped unprecedented power and prosperity, but, inevitably and inexorably, the elements of dissent have propagated until, suddenly, they threaten to upset everything. American institutions are enveloped by the problem of change. This is pronouncedly true of government; it is also true of academic institutions, and of museums.

The Smithsonian Institution is in a fortuitous position to focus on the problem of change. In vast areas of science, history, and art, it possesses the evidence of historical evolution. In no other place is history—history of life, history of man, history of technology, history of art, history of institutions, history of the universe—so tangibly evident. By mandate and unswerving tradition, the Institution has devoted itself to basic research. During the early decades, while the Smithsonian enjoyed pre-eminence as the nation's first center for advanced studies, there was much important activity in experi-

mental research. In the past several decades, during which the Institution has grown into the world's largest museum complex, the products of research have been largely descriptive.

I believe that the Smithsonian now must adopt a different primary concern, that of identifying the causes of change. Cataloguing is not in the spirit of the times. Remaining areas of unclassified *materia naturae* will be described. But now we must ask: why the changes in form, biological and artistic; why the changes in mores, primitive and modern; why the expansion of technology? Perhaps most pertinent is inquiry into causes that have forced changes in American institutions.

In altering its objectives of research, the Smithsonian Institution will, necessarily, change. That it has begun the process is revealed abundantly in the pages of this book. Paul Oehser remarks the contradictions: bureaucratization versus programmatic organization; centralization versus fragmentation; overorganization versus lack of cohesion. The Smithsonian is not a university, though it has academic habits. The Smithsonian is not a museum, though most people identify it as such. If the Smithsonian did not exist, it could not possibly be invented.

These contradictions exist, but they are not the products of some Parkinsonian accretion; on the contrary, they are, quite simply, phenomena of a state of transition. In hippie doctrine, the thing is to be relevant. By seeing our activities programmatically instead of bureaucratically, we should be able to identify those that have lost their relevance to the environment (or society). Taxonomy, for instance, is a program with a purpose, and, like any program, it has its presumed closure; it is not an end in itself. The failing of a bureaucracy is that it cannot cease anything it is doing and thus stultifies the development of the organization. It has proved highly advantageous for the Smithsonian to have its central management and its diverse research enterprises structured according to programmatic themes, and this has caused us, in recent years, to experiment with and to establish new activities that are described by the author.

One way we may become more relevant is through the democratization of our museums. The classical design for the research museum is to increase knowledge through research and to diffuse knowledge through exhibits. This is a powerful ethic and it keeps us honest, for, apart from the milling throngs, we would be so easily lost in our ivory towers. It is unhappily apparent, however, that our museums are not capturing those who most need them—the intellectually deprived, whose homes are barren of Gutenberg's galaxy and whose schools are handicapped by a host of inadequacies. The Mall in Washington should be a place for life and laughter. And, if the poor are intimidated by the grandeur of the museum, we can invent something more relevant, as we have done with the Anacostia Neighborhood Museum.

Founded through an enigma, the Smithsonian Institution may ever retain its air of English irrationality, of muddling through. I certainly hope it will retain its British quality of geniality, of relaxation and lack of "side." Though programs change, style must continue. To repeat a phrase coined for our bicentennial celebration, our aim is still the pursuit of the unfashionable by the unconventional.

Preface

A variety of books have been written about the Smithsonian Institution—histories, biographies, picture books, guide books —and there will be many more. But I have yet to find one that tells the whole story or gets the picture exactly right. The viewpoint makes the difference. It is like the six sightless gentlemen from Indostan in John Godfrey Saxe's poem "The Blind Men and the Elephant," each in turn touching side, tusk, trunk, knee, ear, and tail, and identifying the noble pachyderm as wall, spear, snake, tree, fan, and rope, respectively,

> Though each was partly in the right
> And all were in the wrong.

The present book, in many ways, is also a personal account, for one cannot have been associated with an organization for thirty-five years and write objectively about it consistently. The most difficult task has been to keep abreast of the subject, for the Smithsonian is a living and prolific organism, and, like my young grandson, it gets away from you between visits. It is complex and kaleidoscopic, with its own built-in *son et lumière* system, as it were. I have often surmised that it has a soul as well as a body. The blood that flows through its veins is rejuvenated year by year, even day to day, by new ideas, new people, new methods for doing its job.

I have a feeling that the Smithsonian, with its phenomenal growth, has not been entirely successful, probably inevitably so, in escaping the pitfalls of overorganization and over-management. These excesses are very likely inherent in government, although, for many years, because it is only quasi-governmental, the Institution did largely avoid them and still managed to accomplish a great deal. Today, there is no longer anything pristine about it. I am tempted to—in fact I will—quote a passage from G. D. H. Cole's *Social Theory,* published fifty years ago, which that great entomologist of Harvard William Morton Wheeler used as an epigraph for one of the chapters in his remarkably civilized book *Essays in Philosophical Biology* (Cambridge, Mass.: Harvard University Press, 1939):

> It is necessary to rid ourselves once and for all of the notion that organization is in itself a good thing. It is very easy to fall into the notion that growing complexity is a sign of progress, and that the expanding organization of Society is a sign of the coming of the Cooperative Commonwealth. . . . Organization is a marvelous instrument through which we every day accomplish all manner of achievements which would be inconceivable without it; but it is none the less better to do a thing without organization if we can, or with the minimum of organization that is necessary. . . .
>
> In complex modern communities there are so many things that must be organized that it becomes more than ever important to preserve from organization that sphere in which it adds least to, and is apt to detract most from, our field of self-expression—the sphere of personal relationships and personal conducts.

In my three and a half decades as editor and public-relations officer of the Smithsonian, I had occasion to write scores of articles, press releases, reports, encyclopedia accounts, speeches, one book, and one ode on Smithsonian history and activities. I even did a little ghost-writing. All this is now in the hopper, and in writing the present account I have at times, particularly in the historical sections, drawn liberally from publications over which I toiled in former years. I hope I have fortified the old wine when pouring it into a new bottle. The indispensable sources for anyone writing on the Smithsonian are, of course, the annual reports, which have been remarkably complete since the beginning. I have used them freely. My other principal published sources are listed in the Bibliography.

I am indebted to several of my former colleagues at the Smithsonian Institution for help in writing this book. In particular, Mrs. Nancy Link Powars, longtime publications editor, assisted in rounding up material and performing some of the dull chores. John S. Lea, assistant chief of the Editorial and Publications Division, and Mrs. Eileen McCarthy, in charge of publications distribution, were likewise always helpful. Others have read portions of the manuscript and offered valuable suggestions. George Crossette, my colleague at the National Geographic Society, has been overgenerous with assistance and encouragement. Miss Susan E. Patterson, my former secretary at the National Geographic, did a noble job of typing.

It should be made clear that this is not an "official" book, and it goes forth without necessarily having the blanket approval of the Smithsonian Establishment. Furthermore, I have not attempted to excise all those Oehserisms, which my friends have learned to associate with a mind not altogether free of peculiarities and inconsistencies and whose allegiance wavers somewhere between science and poetry.

I have portrayed the Smithsonian—a great though not perfect institution—as I see it and in historical perspective. No one knows better than I how widely I have missed the mark of the perfect portrait, but I do not expect to live long enough to see any writer do it full justice. If the reader, between the lines, gathers an impression that I distrust some of the newer operations that the Institution has initiated in recent years, not so much in themselves as in their mushrooming proliferation, may he be assured that, being an evolutionist, I am not really opposed to change and that my intent is to be constructive in taking a critical look at the Smithsonian's laudable effort to revitalize and expand its programs.

My affection for the Smithsonian and my faith in its future far eclipse any of its imperfections that I can think of. When a publisher's proofreader called T. E. Lawrence's attention to an inconsistency in the spelling of the name of his she camel in *Revolt in the Desert*—Jedha in one place and Jedhah in another—his reply was, "She was a splendid beast."

PAUL H. OEHSER

McLean, Virginia
August, 1969

Contents

*A map of the Smithsonian Institution buildings in
Washington, D.C., appears on page 183.*

Organization charts appear on pages 82–83.

A section of photographs follows page 116.

I

The Beginnings: James Smithson, His Will, and the Congress of the United States

In the autumn of 1965, in Washington, D.C., the Smithsonian Institution celebrated, with appropriate pomp and some circumstance, the two-hundredth anniversary of the birth of its founder, James Smithson. During a 3-day program, much of it held *al fresco* on the Mall, with its array of Smithsonian buildings, scholars and other well-wishers gathered from all over the world to pay tribute to the obscure Englishman whose vision and somewhat fortuitous bequest generated the complex that today is the Smithsonian Institution. Some of the participants in the event certainly had only a vague notion of who James Smithson was, but all were surely aware of the lengthened shadow that the life of this man had cast over the world of learning. Referring to his own interest in science, Smithson once expressed the modest hope that he might "enlarge those lurid specks in the vast field of darkness." This wish was the seminal purpose of his life, and he sowed its seed in a fertile spot. The Smithson bicentennial celebration, held at a time when the modern age of science had perhaps reached a zenith and when the Smithsonian Institution itself had reached a turning point, focused long overdue world attention on Smithson and his creation, on what he had pre-

3

scribed that he wanted done, and on how his wishes had been interpreted and carried out in the 136 years since his death.

James Smithson was born in Paris, France, in the year 1765, the month and day unknown. The circumstances of his birth were peculiar, to say the least. He was the natural son of the rich and handsome Hugh Smithson, who was made Duke of Northumberland the year after James's birth. His mother was Mrs. Elizabeth Hungerford Keate Macie, a rich widow of Bath.

The Smithsons were an old family remotely related to the Percys, the family of Smithson's wife, and the Duke, by act of Parliament, took the Percy name. Sir Hugh is said to have "sustained his royal rank with great dignity, generosity, and splendor"; he lived a charitable and rollicking life and was buried in Westminster Abbey. In all, he had four illegitimate children, as well as three children by his wife Elizabeth, one of the latter being James's half-brother Hugh Percy, who fought with the British at Bunker Hill and Lexington and who inherited the dukedom.

James's mother was a lineal descendant of King Henry VII through Charles, Duke of Somerset, her great-granduncle, and was a cousin of Hugh Smithson's wife. She was heiress of the Hungerfords of Studley, whose property she inherited in 1766. Nothing is known of Smithson's life in France, but he was taken to England and there naturalized, at the age of 9, and educated. Smithson kept his mother's name and was known as James Lewis Macie at the time he entered Oxford, but by permission of the Crown he later took the name Smithson.

Smithson always retained respect for his noble birth and a sensitivity to the bar sinister. In later years he wrote, "The best blood of England flows in my veins; on my father's side I am a Northumberland, on my mother's I am related to Kings, but this avails me not. My name shall live in the memory of man when the titles of the Northumberlands and the Percys are extinct and forgotten." This, though a rather rash prophecy, since the line of Percys is by no means extinct, struck close to the heart of Smithson's discontent, and it may well have been this resentment of the injustice dealt him that motivated his unusual bequest.

In May, 1782, matriculating as a "gentleman commoner" under the name Macie, James entered Pembroke College, Oxford, whose most famous sons up to that time had been Samuel Johnson and William Blackstone. It is not to be supposed that Sir Hugh was averse to educating his son, but records seem to indicate that the costs of his college education were borne by his mother. He was evidently a serious student and soon acquired an enthusiasm for the natural sciences and a bent for scientific research that influenced all his later life. Perhaps this inclination was due in part to the spirit of the times, for it was a period of intellectual advancement, when ingenious men such as Joseph Priestley, Count Alessandro Volta, Immanuel Kant, Jean Baptiste Lamarck, Johann Wolfgang von Goethe, Baron Georges Cuvier, Sir William Herschel, Sir Humphry Davy, James Watt, and many others were making brilliant discoveries in science and invention and expanding the horizons of philosophic inquiry.

At Pembroke, Smithson became associated with others who shared his interest in science—Davies Gilbert, who was later knighted and became a president of the Royal Society; William Higgins, who anticipated Dalton by his application of the atomic theory to chemistry; and Thomas Beddoes, who became an eminent physician. Although he was thirty-four years younger, Smithson became an intimate friend of the eccentric discoverer of hydrogen Henry Cavendish and worked in his laboratory. Another good friend was the chemist and natural philosopher William Hyde Wollaston.

James was graduated from Pembroke College on May 26, 1786, a few days before his father's death. He was given the degree master of arts. The very next year, at the age of only twenty-two, he was elected a member of the Royal Society. His nomination, signed by five members, including Cavendish, attests to his abilities and to perhaps a certain precociousness:

> James Lewis Macie, Esq., M.A., late of Pembroke College, Oxford, and now of John Street, Golden Square—a gentleman well versed in various branches of Natural Philosophy, and particularly in Chymistry and Mineralogy, being desirous of becoming a Fellow of the Royal Society, we whose names are hereunto subscribed do, from our personal knowledge of his merit, judge him highly worthy of that honor and likely to become a very useful and valuable member.

Under the terms of his naturalization petition granted by the Crown, Smithson was debarred from entering politics, the civil service, the army, and the church—the professions customarily available to gentlemen. It was, therefore, natural that he should find in science a sort of haven, where, in association with men whose interests were similar to his own, he could forget the cloud of his birth. He turned to the serious pursuit of chemistry, which he viewed as an almost virgin field. "Chemistry," he said, "is yet so new a science, what we know of it bears so small a proportion to what we are ignorant of . . . that no researches can be undertaken without producing some facts leading to consequences which extend beyond the boundaries of their immediate object."

SMITHSON'S SCIENTIFIC ACHIEVEMENTS

On July 7, 1791, Smithson read to the Royal Society his first scientific paper, entitled "An Account of Some Chemical Experiments on Tabasheer," tabasheer being a curious concretion found in the hollow of bamboo canes and "an article of importance in the *materia medica* of the ancient Arabians."

He continued his experimentation and made chemical analyses of the calamines. He discovered and analyzed a new zinc ore, which is today called smithsonite in his honor. He subjected various members of the vegetable kingdom—violet, daisy, hollyhock, artichoke, currant, and many others—to minute chemical study. Indeed, it was his habit to analyze in this way practically everything that came to his notice, and he equipped himself with a portable laboratory for that purpose. He assembled a large collection of minerals and rare gems, many of them minute specimens, which when systematically labeled and classified enabled him to compare and readily identify samples that came to hand. His analytical approach is illustrated by an anecdote related by Sir Davies Gilbert in an address before the Royal Society:

> Mr. Smithson declared that, happening to observe a tear gliding down a lady's cheek, he endeavored to catch it on a crystal vessel; that one-half of the drop escaped, but having preserved the other half he submitted it to reagents, and detected what was then called microcosmic salt, with muriate of soda, and, I think, three or four more saline substances, held in solution.

Smithson published, in all, eight scientific papers in the Royal Society's *Philosophical Transactions* (1791–1817), eighteen in the *Annals of Philosophy* (1819–25), and a short note in the *Philosophical Magazine* (1807). Spencer Baird, in an introduction to the published collection of Smithson's papers, stated that the articles embraced "a wide range of research, from the origin of the earth, the nature of the colors of the vegetables and insects, the analysis of minerals and chemicals, to an improved method of constructing lamps or of making coffee." *

In 1784, even before he had left Pembroke, Smithson,

---

* In 1879, the fiftieth anniversary of Smithson's death, twenty-seven papers constituting his entire published scientific work were collected and reprinted in Volume 21 of the *Smithsonian Miscellaneous Collections*.

during a vacation, made a geological expedition to explore Fingal's Cave off the northeast coast of Scotland. The journal that he kept reveals his development as a young scientist, already acquiring diligence in recording his scientific observations of ores and minerals. Though by today's criteria Smithson would probably be called an amateur, he early acquired a fidelity to the experimental method and a high regard for science in general. He tried to record his experiments "precisely as they turned out."

This expedition was the first of many mineralogical field trips that he took throughout Europe during his lifetime. As he traveled around the Continent, he became well known among a large number of scientists and corresponded and exchanged views with such men as Dominique François Jean Arago, the French physicist and revolutionist; Ottavio Tozzetti, the Italian botanist; Giovanni Fabbroni, the Florentine naturalist, chemist, and engineer; and Anton Vassalli-Eandi, inventor of an electrometer. Samuel P. Langley, in his memoir on Smithson, noted that it was Arago, in fact, who recorded an interesting sidelight on Smithson's habits. It seems that, during his later life, Smithson acquired a taste for gambling. "Save for a few hours given to repose," said Arago, his life "was regularly divided between the most interesting scientific researches and gaming. It was a source of great regret to me that this learned experimentalist should devote half of so valuable a life to a course so little in harmony with an intellect whose wonderful powers called forth the admiration of the world around him." Smithson did not, however, allow this pastime to fritter away his fortune, and apparently he never lost any great amount in excess of his winnings.

A reasonable evaluation of Smithson's scientific achievements, given by Dr. Frank Wigglesworth Clarke, former chief chemist of the U.S. Geological Survey, was also recorded in Langley's memoir on Smithson:

The most notable feature of Smithson's writings, from the standpoint of the modern analytical chemist, is the success obtained with the most primitive and unsatisfactory appliances. In Smithson's day, chemical apparatus was undeveloped, and instruments were improvised from such materials as lay readiest at hand. With such instruments, and with crude reagents, Smithson obtained analytical results of the most creditable character, and enlarged our knowledge of many mineral species. In his time the native carbonate and silicate of zinc were confounded as one species under the name "calomine"; but his researches distinguish between the two minerals, which are now known as smithsonite and calamine respectively.

To theory Smithson contributed little, if anything; but from a theoretical point of view the tone of his writings is singularly modern. His work was mostly done before Dalton had announced the atomic theory, and yet Smithson saw clearly that a law of definite proportions must exist, although he did not attempt to account for it. His ability as a reasoner is best shown in his paper upon the Kirkdale bone cave, which [Granville] Penn had sought to interpret by reference to the Noachian deluge. A clearer and more complete demolition of Penn's views could hardly be written today. Smithson was gentle with his adversary, but none the less thorough for all his moderation. He is not to be classed among the leaders of scientific thought; but his ability, and the usefulness of his contributions to knowledge, cannot be doubted.

A more recent account of Smithson's contributions is provided by Leonard Carmichael and J. C. Long in *James Smithson and the Smithsonian Story:*

Smithson's intellectual curiosity was endless. A lesson which may be learned from his career is that everything in the material world is worthy of study. The very catholicity of his view kept him from concentrating on any particular field. But his example served to enhance his reputation in his own time, and his studies gave hints which were useful to future research chemists.

THE TEMPER OF THE TIMES

Through much of the turbulent period of the French Revolution, Smithson apparently lived in Paris, and at least in the early stages of that struggle his sympathies were with the revolutionists. He was still a young man, in temperament sensitive to the social and political injustices that lay at the bottom of the world unrest. Although his older half-brother, Hugh Percy, had fought at Bunker Hill, James was only ten years old at the time, and the American Revolution probably made even less of an impression on him than it did on most of his older countrymen. The struggle in Europe, however, was different, and living through it strengthened his internationalist and republican philosophy. In 1792, three years after the storming of the Bastille, he wrote from Paris:

> *Ça ira* is growing to be the song of England, of Europe, as well as of France. Men of every rank are joining in the chorus. Stupidity and guilt have had a long reign, and it begins, indeed, to be time for justice and common sense to have their turn. . . . Mr. Louis Bourbon is still at Paris, and the office of King is not yet abolished, but they daily feel the inutility, or rather great inconvenience, of continuing it, and its duration will probably not be long. May other nations, at the time of their reforms, be wise enough to cast off, at first, the contemptible incumbrance.

In France, as a British subject, he wisely kept his activities on a philosophical level, and it is not known how many or which of the revolutionists he may have known. However, he was able to avoid involvement for only a few years. When he returned to the Continent on a mineral-collecting expedition in 1807, he was imprisoned by the Danish Government, which at that time was supporting Napoleon against Britain. It was an unfortunate incident, but since Smithson was a Britisher, though on a peaceful civilian mission, it was not easy to convince the Danes that he was not a spy. Incarceration was a rigorous experience for the innocent James, and he became ill. Finally, after his English friends intervened and the Danes realized that Smithson was a rather famous man, the King of Denmark set him free. Even then, he had difficulty in getting back to England. He was held captive again in Hamburg and did not reach England until 1812.

Influences on Smithson from the New World are mainly conjectural. He never visited America. He must have come in contact with some of the American sympathizers of the French Revolution, perhaps Thomas Paine, who was in England and France during the years 1787 to 1802, and the American poet and patriot Joel Barlow, who became a French citizen in 1792, acted as President James Madison's minister plenipotentiary to France, and lived on intimate terms with the democratic leaders, French sympathizers, and philosophical deists. In fact, it is unlikely that, in his peregrinations around Europe, Smithson would have missed so well-known and colorful a figure as Barlow.

In Smithson's library at the time of his death were three books that indicated he had some interest in and knowledge of the United States—a paper by DuPont de Nemours on education in the United States; J. Harriott's *Struggles Through Life, Exemplified in the Various Travels and Adventures in Europe, Asia, Africa, and America;* and Isaac Weld's *Travels Through the States of North America and the Provinces of Upper and Lower Canada, During the Years 1795, 1796, and 1797.*

There was probably no one event that persuaded James Smithson to bequeath his fortune to the United States. He was a man of his times, and his reasons were no doubt a result of the pervasive influences that his age brought to bear on an independent personality who wanted to do something original and lasting for his fellow man.

It was a time when the Romantic poets, no doubt familiar with the works of William Bartram and Hector St. John de Crèvecoeur, saw America as a utopia, where people could be saved from Europe's corruption and injustices begotten of antiquity and outworn social systems. Joel Barlow saw an "Athens rising on the banks of the Potomac." Coleridge and Southey dreamed of a "pantisocracy" on the Susquehanna. Blake would have the Ohio wash from him the stains of the Thames. Goethe wrote: "America, you're better off than/ Our continent, the old./You have no castles which are fallen,/No basalt to behold." Shelley apostrophized America as the place where "Freedom and Truth are Worshiped," where "the multitudinous earth shall sleep beneath thy shade." Chateaubriand brought back from his voyage to America romantic pictures of the physical virginity of the country, the wilderness grandeur of the Mohawk and the Niagara. The new, optimistic spirit in the air of Europe was eloquently expressed by Wordsworth: "Bliss was it in that dawn to be alive, but to be young was very Heaven."

Other influences have been suggested as well, but they, too, cannot be documented. There is a tradition, for example, apparently started by Louis Agassiz when he was a regent of the Smithsonian Institution, that Smithson had intended to leave his money to the Royal Society, which had been good to him but with whose officers he was said to have had a quarrel. There is no foundation for this theory.

Another influence may have been the Royal Institution of London, established in 1800 by the American Benjamin Thompson (Count Rumford) "for diffusing the knowledge and facilitating the general introduction of useful mechanical inventions and improvements and for teaching by courses of philosophical lectures and experiments the application of science to the common purposes of life." Smithson was a charter member of the Royal Institution and was thoroughly familiar with its purposes. His prescription for *his* institution—"the increase and diffusion of knowledge among men"—is broader and more succinct, but there is a parallel. Both are reminiscent of a phrase in George Washington's farewell address in which he urged his countrymen to "promote institutions for the general diffusion of knowledge."

But the fundamental impulse that led Smithson to the unusual disposition of his fortune was, I believe, his feeling that his own country, by denying him his noble birthright and the normal fulfillment of a life in England suitable to his talents and inclinations, had let him down. He may well have felt that he had to compensate to the world and demonstrate that he could perpetuate his name by holding to a high idealism and a faith in mankind and rising above the disappointments and the frustrations he suffered.

"I THEN BEQUEATH . . ."

Smithson never married, a singularly important fact, for, as a reading of his will shows, if he had married, there would have been no Smithsonian Institution. As a single man, he was free to travel around Europe, befriend scientists, collect minerals, and indulge his hobbies. During his later years, he lived, probably in some style, in the wealthy city of Genoa, Italy. In 1826, he was sixty-one years of age and his health was failing. He was residing in London that year, and on October 23 he made his will, drawing it up in his own deliberate hand:

THE WILL OF JAMES SMITHSON

I James Smithson Son to Hugh, first Duke of Northumberland, & Elizabeth, Heiress of the Hungerfords of Studley, & Niece to Charles the proud Duke of Somerset, now residing in

Bentinck Street, Cavendish Square, do this twenty-third day of October, one thousand eight hundred and twenty-six, make this my last Will and Testament:

I bequeath the whole of my property of every nature & kind soever to my bankers, Messrs. Drummonds of Charing Cross, in trust, to be disposed of in the following manner, and I desire of my said Executors to put my property under the management of the Court of Chancery.

To John Fitall, formerly my Servant, but now employed in the London Docks, and residing at No. 27, Jubilee Place, North Mile End, old town, in consideration of his attachment & fidelity to me, & the long & great care he has taken of my effects, & my having done but very little for him, I give and bequeath the Annuity or annual sum of One hundred pounds sterling for his life, to be paid to him quarterly, free of legacy duty & all other deductions, the first payment to be made to him at the expiration of three months after my death. . . .

To Henry James Hungerford, my Nephew, heretofore called Henry James Dickinson, son of my late brother, Lieutenant-Colonel Henry Louis Dickinson, now residing with Mr. Auboin, at Bourg la Reine, near Paris, I give and bequeath for his life the whole of the income arising from my property of every nature & kind whatever, after the payment of the above Annuity, & after the death of John Fitall, that Annuity likewise, the payments to be made to him at the time the interest or dividends become due on the Stocks or other property from which the income arises.

Should the said Henry James Hungerford have a child or children, legitimate or illegitimate, I leave to such child or children, his or their heirs, executors, & assigns, after the death of his, or her, or their Father, the whole of my property of every kind absolutely & forever, to be divided between them, if there is more than one, in the manner their father shall judge proper, or, in case of his omitting to decide this, as the Lord Chancellor shall judge proper.

Should my said Nephew, Henry James Hungerford, marry, I empower him to make a jointure.

In the case of the death of my said Nephew without leaving a child or children, or the death of the child or children he may have had under the age of twenty-one years or intestate, I then bequeath the whole of my property subject to the Annuity of One Hundred pounds to John Fitall, & for the security & payment of which I mean Stock to remain in this Country, to the United States of America, to found at Washington, under the name of the Smithsonian Institution, an Establishment for the increase & diffusion of knowledge among men. . . .

Smithson lived only three years longer. He died in Genoa on June 26, 1829. Six years later, his nephew, Henry James Hungerford, then known as Baron Eunice de la Batut, also died. Destiny entered the picture again: Hungerford was unmarried and left no heirs, and so the final provision of Smithson's will became operative. Had Hungerford left even illegitimate children (a conscientious search failed to disclose any), there would have been no Smithsonian Institution.

Smithson was buried in a little cemetery belonging to the English church at Genoa, for he had been reared a Protestant. There his remains stayed for three-quarters of a century. In 1900, the Smithsonian learned that the cemetery was to be moved because of the encroachment of a municipal stone quarry. A special delegation, headed by Alexander Graham Bell, then a Smithsonian regent, brought the relics to the United States, and with due ceremony they were entombed within a small mortuary chapel near the main entrance to the original Smithsonian Building. Today it is sometimes said that the only person buried in downtown Washington, D.C., is James Smithson, a bastard Englishman, whose great contribution was to raise the dignity of man by his consummate faith in the promise of a new nation only half a century old. He dreamed a dream that came true.

THE FOUNDING STRUGGLE

It was one thing to conceive the Smithsonian Institution, as Smithson did, with a few strokes of the pen. It was quite another to bring it into being, and this task plagued Congress for more than a decade. Seven weeks after Hungerford's death, the U.S. Government was formally notified of the Smithson bequest. In a message to Congress in December, 1835, President Andrew Jackson announced the gift but added that he had no authority to accept it. Thereupon began a long and tedious debate among the legislators, first as to whether the bequest should be accepted at all, and second as to what form and character the Smithsonian Institution should actually take.

In the Senate, the matter was referred to the Committee on the Judiciary, which decided that Smithson's bequest was valid and that "the United States would be entertained in the court of chancery of England to assert their claim to the fund as trustees for the purpose of founding the charitable institution at Washington to which it is destined by the donor." Some members dissented. William C. Preston of South Carolina thought that Smithson's intention was to found a university but that the United States had no power to receive the money. John C. Calhoun, also of South Carolina, expressed the opinion that "it was beneath their dignity to receive presents from anyone." But others, including James Buchanan of Pennsylvania, advocated acceptance, and eventually, on May 2, 1836, the resolution to accept the legacy passed the Senate.

In the House of Representatives, the matter of the Smithson gift was laid before a special committee under the chairmanship of John Quincy Adams. Adams, who became the most effective Smithsonian protagonist, saw the far-reaching implications of the action of James Smithson. He succeeded in overcoming the House opposition by his eloquence and successfully steered the passage of the House bill. The actions of the Senate and the House were combined in one bill, which President Jackson signed on July 1, 1836, authorizing the prosecution of the claim to the legacy. An appropriation of $10,000 was made to cover the costs.

The President forthwith appointed the eminent Richard Rush of Pennsylvania, an experienced diplomat, who had been minister to both England and France, as agent of the U.S. Government to go to London and "assert the claim of the United States." This he did expeditiously and adroitly. In less than two years, he successfully saw the friendly suit through the court of chancery, which, not noted for its speed, was eight hundred cases in arrears at the time. The estate of Smithson transferred to Rush consisted of securities worth more than £106,000 sterling. When the costs of the suit had been deducted, the remainder was converted into gold sovereigns, and, on July 17, 1838, packed in £1,000 bags in eleven boxes, was shipped aboard the packet *Mediator* for New York, where it arrived on August 29. Three days later, the gold, amounting to £104,960 8s. 6d., was delivered to the U.S. Mint in Philadelphia, where it was recoined into American money. It amounted to $508,318.46.

Just what the Smithsonian Institution was to be, however, was still unsettled. On December 6, 1838, President Martin Van Buren announced to Congress that the Smithson fund had been received and reminded the legislators of "the obligation now devolving upon the United States to fulfill the object of the bequest." But Congress was faced with more pressing problems, for the nation was in the midst of the worst economic depression it had known, the Panic of 1837. There had been overexpansion in industry; the widespread canal-building enterprises were not paying off; the working classes were restless; poverty was rampant. The legislators were trying desperately to bring the country out of the slump, and it is no wonder that they took eight years to determine the disposal of Smithson's gift.

But Congress's bewilderment was not surprising. The gift of half a million dollars, a sizable sum for those days, had no precedent. It had been sudden and unexpected and was to be used for a rather vague purpose. In the United States in 1838, there were only three scientific foundations that pretended to be national in scope. These were the American Philosophical Society, at Philadelphia, patterned after the Royal Society of London and dating from the time of Benjamin Franklin; the American Academy of Arts and Sciences, at Boston, established directly after the Revolution; and the Franklin Institute, at Philadelphia, organized in 1824. There were also a few private scientific establishments, such as Bartram's Botanic Garden, Rittenhouse's Observatory, and Peale's Natural History Museum, and a number of local scientific societies in the larger cities. In the government itself, science had made but a small beginning in the U.S. Coast Survey, which was created by President Thomas Jefferson in 1807. Jefferson's Lewis and Clark Expedition, though ostensibly undertaken in the interests of promoting commerce, had provided, somewhat surreptitiously, for a scientific reconnaissance of the western frontier. And the second government-sponsored "scientific" expedition, that of Captain Charles Wilkes, had not yet made its impact; it did not return from its round-the-world exploration until 1842, and the full publication of its 20-volume report was not completed until 1876. Scientific matters were, however, coming more and more to the attention of Congress and the people, particularly in the field of invention. Samuel F. B. Morse had just applied for a patent on his telegraph and had asked the government for $30,000 to subsidize a 50-mile demonstration telegraph system. The lawmakers took five years to approve this appropriation. Other inventions were claiming public attention, and, although it cannot be denied that science still had its stronghold in Europe, the United States was particularly responsive to the wave of intellectual activity that seemed to be coming its way.

The Smithson bequest coincided with this wave. In the House of Representatives, John Quincy Adams, who possessed an abiding and militant devotion to science, was made chairman of the 9-man committee to which the Smithson matter was referred. Adams had strong convictions on the subject. As President, he had dreamed of Washington's becoming a world center for scholarship and for the arts and sciences. In Smithson's legacy, he saw an opportunity for the realization of this dream. However, he was especially opposed to using any of the money for "the endowment of any school, college, university, or ecclesiastical establishment." Instead, he thought that Smithson's wishes would best be carried out by the creation of an astronomical observatory, with instruments and a library. A university, however, was favored by many intellectual leaders, and for a while it seemed that such a proposal would win. Senator Asher Robbins of Rhode Island, in an eloquent speech before the Senate on January 10, 1839, proposed the creation of "an institution of which there is no model either in this country or Europe, to provide such a course of education and discipline as would give to the faculties of the human mind an improvement far beyond what they afterwards attain in any of the professional pursuits." His proposal was fine but indefinite, and the matter was tabled until the following session of Congress.

In the meantime, Adams, campaigning for the Smithsonian cause, delivered in the fall of 1839 two lectures at Quincy and Boston, Massachusetts, adulating the high purposes of the Smithson bequest, arguing for his own ideas, and warning against the danger of the dissipation of the Smithson money through delayed action. He laid out in detail before his audiences the whole history of the case. On the following March 5, in an elaborate report, he reviewed the situation again before the House of Representatives, renewing his strong argument against the creation of a school or college. "We should in no case," he said, "avail ourselves of a stranger's munificence to rear our children." He still favored the observatory plan, but could bring about no conclusive action at that session.

Those most interested in the Smithsonian Institution began to despair. On November 26, 1841, Richard Rush wrote to his friend and former secretary Benjamin Ogle Tayloe:

> Alas for the Smithsonian Institution! I labored anxiously and hard for the *fund*, and after receiving the full gold on the other side of the water, more in value than the original bequest, through the fortunate sale I made of the English Government stock, in which the testator's money stood, never lost sight of it until it was all safely deposited in the United States Mint; little dreaming, however, that there the matter was to rest for years. But so it seems—so it was, and fortunate will it be if the fund itself, at an era of such dishonesty and hocus-pocus, is not made way with, or dilapidated, before any public use whatever is made of the beneficent bequest. Congress has slept over the subject, and the Executive too.

Little progress was made until 1844 when, on June 6, the Joint Library Committee of Congress introduced a bill providing that the original amount of the Smithson bequest be considered as a permanent loan to the United States at 6 per cent interest; that the interest that had accrued up to July 1, 1844 ($178,604), be used for the erection of buildings and the enclosure of grounds for the Smithsonian Institution; that the business of the establishment be conducted by a board of twelve managers from different states or territories; that a plain and substantial building be erected, with rooms for a museum, library, chemical laboratory, lectures, and arboretum; and that all objects of natural history belonging to the United States in Washington be transferred to the Institution. It provided further that a superintendent should be appointed who would also be "professor" of agriculture and horticulture. There would be additional professors of natural history, chemistry, astronomy, and similar subjects. Experiments would be made to determine the utility of new fruits, plants, and vegetables. Students would be admitted free. These provisions were amplified in another bill introduced in the Senate on December 12, and another period of discussion began. In a brilliant speech, the eminent jurist Rufus Choate of Massachusetts opposed a school or college as being unnecessary and too utilitarian but approved the lecture and library provisions of the bill. "Does not the whole history of civilization concur to declare that a various and ample library is one of the surest, most constant, most permanent and most economical instrumentalities to increase and diffuse knowledge?" He expressed his hope that Smithson's gift would be used to accumulate a grand and noble public library, equal to any in the world, and indicated that he would amend the bill accordingly. The pros and cons argued for a few days longer. On January 23, 1845, the Senate passed the bill. It was sent to the House, but there, in the hurry of a short session of Congress, it was once again left undisposed of.

The following year, in the Twenty-ninth Congress, a new bill, embracing the principal features of the old one but adding several new provisions, was sponsored by Robert Dale Owen of Indiana. It included a section providing for a sort of normal school to train teachers in natural science and in "the most useful of all modern sciences—the humble yet world-subduing science of primary education." The library provision was retained. Scientific research was to be encouraged, and publications in science and history, pamphlets, magazines, and manuals were authorized. Owen made an impassioned plea for his bill and took the congressmen to task for their dilatoriness in handling the Smithson bequest. The debate opened again in full force. George W. Jones and Andrew Johnson, both of Tennessee, and Orlando B. Ficklin of Illinois attacked

the Owen bill, while Jefferson Davis of Mississippi, Frederick
P. Stanton of Tennessee, and Joseph R. Ingersoll of Pennsylvania vigorously defended it. Various amendments were offered. The provisions for a normal school, professors, lecturers,
and students were stricken out. John Quincy Adams agreed to
drop his observatory appeal, since in the meantime the U.S.
Naval Observatory had been organized. The provision for
lectures was rejected. The annual appropriation for the library
was increased. Representative George Perkins Marsh from
Vermont, one of the nineteenth century's intellectually great
men, added his weight to the argument, particularly on behalf
of the library, in "one of the best speeches ever delivered in
the House," according to Adams. An amendment was
adopted specifying that the government collections deposited
in the institution should be known as the National Museum.
Finally, a substitute bill was agreed upon, and the House
narrowly passed it, 85 to 76. In August, the Senate considered
the bill and passed it by a vote of 26 to 13. It was signed by
President James K. Polk on August 10, 1846. The Smithsonian Institution was at last established—twenty years after
James Smithson drew his will.

Lengthy and fumbling as these deliberations in Congress
were, in the light of history they take on importance. They
helped crystallize in the minds of national leaders the idea
that science is a proper interest of government. It was an idea
that, in the United States, had its genesis with Thomas Jefferson and was militantly abetted by John Quincy Adams. The
debate over the Smithson bequest brought it to public attention, with Adams the indefatigable gadfly. Today, as the
Secretary of the Smithsonian wrote in the Institution's 1951
annual report:

No one dares question that concept. Present-day exigencies
have forced us to recognize that there are certain types of

scientific investigation which are essential . . . and that these must not be left to haphazard and uncertain backing of private individuals and organizations. . . . They must be publicly and continuously financed so long as science continues to be so strategically integrated with our politics, economics, and social well-being.

John Quincy Adams was one of the few who foresaw this necessity with broad and prophetic understanding. In *The Adams Family* (Boston: Little, Brown, 1930), James Truslow Adams wrote that

> Adams's love of science was pure and disinterested, but it was closely connected in his mind with the problem of government. . . . If democracy were to succeed it would have to be by bringing up the general level to such a point as to make the people intellectually and morally capable of doing so. In a democracy, therefore, the spread of enlightenment was an essential part of the problem of government.

The organic Act of August 10, 1846, establishing the Smithsonian Institution provided the framework on which to build. Although it contained imperfections, it also demonstrated an honest attempt on the part of Congress to interpret and implement the wishes of Smithson, whose directions were, after all, open-ended. "Increase and diffusion of knowledge" could mean many things, and it is certainly to the credit of those antebellum lawmakers that they did as well as they did, despite all the behind-the-scenes lobbying and feuding that went on in an attempt to make the Smithsonian something other than what it finally became.

As finally signed into law, the Act contained eleven provisions:

1. Setting up the Smithsonian Establishment.
2. Providing for the disposition of the Smithsonian funds.

3. Providing for a Board of Regents, Chancellor, Executive Committee, and Secretary.
4. Providing for the selection of a site for a Smithsonian building.
5. Providing for the erection of the building.
6. Transferring to the Institution all objects of art, natural history, etc., belonging to the United States in Washington and also the minerals, books, manuscripts, and other property of James Smithson, which had been received by the government.
7. Outlining certain duties of the Secretary and providing for salaries.
8. Authorizing stated and special meetings of members of the Institution and specifying that an appropriation not exceeding an average of $25,000 a year, from the interest of the Smithsonian fund, be made for the gradual formation of a library.
9. Authorizing the managers of the Institution to spend income of the Smithson fund "as they deem best suited for the promotion of the purpose of James Smithson."
10. Directing that one copy of all publications copyrighted under the acts of Congress shall be deposited in a Smithsonian library and one copy in the Library of Congress.
11. Reserving the right of Congress to alter, amend, add to, or repeal any of the provisions of the Act.

The person most gratified at the outcome was perhaps John Quincy Adams, who, after serving as President of the United States, had come back to Congress in 1831 to serve seventeen years as Representative from Massachusetts. Representing the intellectualism of the Eastern seaboard against the pragmatism of some of his frontier compatriots, he had fought hard for the Smithsonian Institution. It is difficult to imagine what the Smithsonian would have been without his wisdom and vision.

He lived only a year and a half after the Smithsonian Act was passed and so did not witness its fruition under the leadership of Joseph Henry, its first Secretary. In one of his last speeches in the House, Adams said, "Of all the foundations of establishments for pious or charitable uses which ever signalized the spirit of the age, none can be found more deserving the approbation of mankind than the Smithsonian Institution." The words of this tribute were among those carved on the marble panels flanking the south entrance of the Smithsonian's Museum of History and Technology building in 1963.

II

Joseph Henry, His "Programme," and the Early Years

The Act incorporating the Smithsonian delegated the job of conducting the business of the Institution to a Board of Regents composed of fifteen members: the Vice-President of the United States, the Chief Justice of the United States, and the Mayor of the city of Washington,* all ex officio members; three members of the U.S. Senate (appointed by the President of the Senate); three members of the House of Representatives (appointed by the Speaker of the House); and six citizen members, two of whom had to be residents of the District of Columbia and four of whom had to be from different states (appointed by joint resolution of the Senate and the House). The officers of the Board of Regents were designated Chancellor (the presiding officer of the Board) and Secretary (the executive officer of the Institution).

The three ex officio members of the first board were Vice-President George Mifflin Dallas of Pennsylvania, Chief Justice

* A succession of Washington mayors from 1846 to 1871 served as Smithsonian regents ex officio, but, in the latter year, the office of mayor was abolished, to be replaced by the office of governor, which in turn was abolished in 1874. The last of the two governors who served as regents was the stormy Alexander Roby ("Boss") Shepherd. Under the commission form of government next imposed, the District had no mayor. The new D.C. Government of 1967 again provided for a mayor, but by that time the Smithsonian Act had been amended to remove this ex officio member from the board of regents, making the number officially fourteen.

26

Roger B. Taney of Maryland, and Mayor William W. Seaton; the members from the Senate were George Evans of Maine, Isaac S. Pennybacker of Virginia, and Sidney Breese of Illinois; the three representatives were William J. Hough of New York, Robert Dale Owen of Indiana, and Henry W. Hilliard of Alabama. Rufus Choate of Massachusetts, Gideon Hawley of New York, Richard Rush of Pennsylvania, William C. Preston of South Carolina, and Alexander Dallas Bache and Joseph G. Totten of Washington, D.C., served as the six citizen regents. At their first meeting, on September 7, 1846, less than a month after the Act became law, they elected Vice-President Dallas Chancellor.*

THE FIRST SECRETARY

The regents then faced the problem of choosing a Secretary, and they set their standards high. They wanted a man with weight of character as well as a high grade of talent. He had to possess "eminent scientific and general requirements" and be capable of "advancing science and promoting letters by original research and effort, well qualified to act as a respected channel of communication between the Institution and scientific and literary individuals and societies in this and foreign countries." Furthermore, he had to have competency as an executive officer and a knowledge of the world.

One of the most fortunate events in the history of American science was the selection of Professor Joseph Henry of Princeton to fill this important and difficult post. Henry was a logical choice. Though then only forty-nine years old, he was well known in the scientific world. He had already made a reputation as a "natural philosopher" (physicist) through his basic discoveries in the field of electromagnetism. The astronomer Simon Newcomb once stated that "Henry was the first

* By custom, the office of Chancellor has always been held by either the Vice-President or the Chief Justice.

American after Franklin to reach high eminence in physical science." Since 1832, he had been professor of natural philosophy at the College of New Jersey (now Princeton University), where he not only distinguished himself by his originality as a teacher but also carried on research in electromagnetism and invented the telegraph, continuing experiments he had previously conducted while associated with the Albany Academy in Albany, New York. He discovered the principle of self-induction, an honor he shared with his British contemporary Michael Faraday. He had traveled in Europe and had met Faraday and many other eminent scientists. He had had twenty years of academic life, and he loved it. Henry was, in 1846, at the peak of his scientific career, and he had little reason for desiring a change. Although he was filled with doubts and reluctant to leave the salubrious life at Princeton, the offer of the Smithsonian Secretaryship was a tremendous challenge. Something inherent in the idealism of the Smithson legacy appealed to him.

The Board of Regents confirmed Henry's appointment as Secretary at its meeting on December 3, 1846. Henry had already given much thought to what such an institution might be under the broad provisions of James Smithson's will, and at the request of the regents, he had prepared a plan of organization encompassing his ideas as to how the Smithsonian might effectively operate.

Joseph Henry was born in Albany, New York, on December 17, 1797, a descendant of Scottish Puritans who had settled in eastern New York about the time of the American Revolution. As a youth, his first leanings were not in the direction of science but were toward literature, and he developed a fondness for the theater. He was not particularly studious. His family was not affluent, and he worked to supplement their income, at one time as an apprentice to a silversmith and watchmaker.

It was quite fortuitous that Henry turned to science. When

he was sixteen, a friend lent him *Lectures on Experimental Philosophy, Astronomy, and Chemistry, Intended Chiefly for the Use of Young People,* by George Gregory, an English clergyman, and Henry's interest was so aroused that he determined to pursue these matters of "natural philosophy." He began to study, first at a night school and then at the Albany Academy, earning his way by teaching in a country school and later serving as tutor to the family of General Stephen Van Rensselaer and to Henry James the elder, at that time a pupil at the Academy. Next he accepted an offer to participate in a road-surveying expedition across the western part of New York from West Point to Lake Erie. This trip gave him valuable experience and served also to fortify his somewhat precarious health. When he returned, he was engaged as a teacher at Albany Academy, where, in 1828, at the age of thirty-one, he was appointed professor of mathematics. At the Academy, he began his famous experiments in electromagnetism. In May, 1830, he married his cousin Harriet L. Alexander of Schenectady. Two years later, he was called to Princeton.

Even before he left Albany, Henry had begun to publish. He was only twenty-eight when his first scientific paper, "On the Production of Cold by the Rarefaction of Air," appeared in the *Transactions* of the Albany Institute. Other maiden efforts grew principally out of his interest in geology and meteorology. For example, his third paper, published in 1829 in the *Transactions,* was entitled "Topographical Sketch of the State of New York; Designed Chiefly to Show the General Elevations and Depressions of Its Surface." Later, however, when he began to make pioneering discoveries in electromagnetism, electrodynamic induction, the cohesion of liquids, and other fields, he developed a caution toward hastily publishing the results of his research, a habit that, in some instances, deprived him of proper credit for his discoveries. He held pure scientific research in high regard, an admirable trait in a world dominated by utilitarianism. He believed his special forte was to expand the boundaries of knowledge, leaving to perhaps less imaginative but more enterprising men the task of applying new knowledge to the uses of mankind. He did not even take out patents on discoveries that might well have made him a fortune. He was more interested in having the approval of his scientific equals than the applause of the public. He saw clearly the value of abstract science and was eloquent in its defense. "He who loves truth for its own sake," he once wrote, "feels that its highest claims are lowered and its moral influence marred by being continually summoned to the bar of immediate and palpable utility."

So the Smithsonian regents, in making their choice, were not operating blindly. They knew about Joseph Henry, his abilities, and his reputation. And Henry, once he had made up his mind to accept the post, was ready. Before his appointment, one of the regents, Alexander Dallas Bache, had asked his opinion "as to the meaning of the will" and whether he had a plan of "realizing the intention of the donor." Henry gave the answer in the form of a well-thought-out "Programme of Organization of the Smithsonian Institution," which he circulated in preliminary draft to a number of learned societies and individuals throughout the country for criticism. He reported that in every case the program received their "unqualified approbation." The regents approved the plan in principle on December 4, 1846, and in a more refined form on December 13, 1847. Because this plan governed the name and nature of the Institution from the beginning and became the foundation of its development, it is important to consider it in some detail.

Even as early as 1856, Henry stated, "This programme . . . has become the settled policy of the Institution." He realized, however, that it was not perfect, but he had to be practical. "It is not contended," he wrote, "that the plan of organization is in all respects what could be wished . . . but in establishing an institution in which various opinions were to be regarded, the question was not, what, in the abstract, was the best, but the best which, under the circumstances, could be adopted." Henry prefaced his "programme" with fourteen "general considerations which should serve as a guide in adopting a Plan of Organization." One suggestion was that the Institution undertake only programs that could not be adequately carried out by the existing institutions of the country. It may be argued whether Smithsonian administrations have always hewed to this line, but they have, at least, perennially tried to do so. As recently as 1966, the Secretary of the Smithsonian, in his introduction to the symposium *Knowledge Among Men,* wrote:

If the Smithsonian Institution has a motto, aside from the enigmatic and Sibylline "increase and diffusion of knowledge among men," it should be *the pursuit of the unfashionable by the unconventional. . . .* In its history the Smithsonian has always tried to do only what for various reasons other organizations or agencies were not doing, and to husband its resources of manpower toward the accomplishment of abstract and original study.

Henry's plan emphasized further that the Smithson bequest was intended for the benefit of mankind and that, therefore, "all unnecessary expenditure on local objects would be a perversion of the trust." The U.S. Government was to act as trustee to carry out the design of Smithson; it would not, however, be a national establishment in the usual sense, but, rather, an establishment dedicated to the pursuit of knowledge, bearing and perpetuating its founder's name. The objectives of the Institution were clear—to increase and diffuse knowledge among men. Inasmuch as Smithson's will did not define or restrict in any way the particular kind of knowledge to be diffused and augmented, no branch of knowledge could rightly be excluded from its share of attention. Said Henry, in an early report, "Smithson was well aware that knowledge should not be viewed as existing in isolated parts, but as a whole, each portion of which throws light on all the others, and that the tendency of all is to improve the human mind, and to give it new sources of power and enjoyment."

With these liberal principles in mind, Henry proposed that the Institution, to fulfill its charge of increasing knowledge, should stimulate men of talent to carry on original research by offering suitable rewards for memoirs containing new truths, which would then be published in a series of quarto volumes called "Smithsonian Contributions to Knowledge," and to appropriate annually a portion of the Smithsonian's income for particular research carried out under the direction of suitable persons. To fulfill the charge of diffusing knowledge, he proposed that the Institution publish a series of periodical reports on the progress of the different branches of knowledge as well as occasionally publishing separate treatises on subjects of general interest.

His course of action thus outlined, Henry set about getting things in motion. His first job was overseeing the construction of the Smithsonian Building, which proved to be a lengthy and frustrating task. Even though plans by the prominent architect James Renwick, Jr., had been approved soon after Henry's appointment, it was eleven years before the Smithsonian staff moved into the building, and even then construction was not complete. However, under Henry's able direction, the Smithsonian was a going concern long before the building was finished.

THREE BASIC PROJECTS

Within the first three years, Henry had inaugurated three projects basic to his plan: the establishment of a system of meteorological observations throughout the country, centered at the Smithsonian; the organization of a system for the international exchange of scientific publications; and the beginnings of a publication program.

Henry outlined his meteorological proposals in his annual report for 1848. The plan was to obtain weather reports from a great network of voluntary observers scattered over the country, particularly for the purpose of assembling long-range data on climate and weather from stations in every region. In this way, the studies would furnish a sound foundation upon which the science of meteorology could build. It was an original idea, and one that eminently illustrated the principle of cooperation inherent in Henry's program. It gave the people in general a kind of grass-roots stake in this new Institution, about which most of them knew so little. Henry enlisted the active support of leading meteorologists of the country, one of whom, Professor Arnold Guyot, a Swiss scientist who had just come to the United States, was entrusted with the job of selecting and ordering the instruments required and preparing a set of "Directions for Meteorological Observations" to serve as a guide for the observers.

There would be, Henry said, three classes of observers:

One class, without instruments, to observe the face of the sky as to its clearness, the extent of cloud, the direction and force of wind, the beginning and end of rain, snow, etc. A second class, furnished with thermometers, who besides making the observations above mentioned, will record variations of temperature. The third class, furnished with full sets of instruments, to observe all the elements at present deemed important in the science of meteorology.

By 1852, the voluntary observers reporting directly to the Smithsonian numbered about two hundred. Then the states of New York and Massachusetts cooperated by setting up weather stations with instruments at various academies; although these stations had state support, they were directed by the Institution. Further observations were made at a hundred or so military posts of the United States under the direction of the surgeon general of the U.S. Army. Separate series of observations, recorded by exploring and surveying parties, were reported back to the Institution. In Canada, observations were made at various posts of the Hudson's Bay Company. Stations reached to Nova Scotia, Panama, and Bermuda, and there was even one observer at Ascención, Paraguay. "As a part of the system of meteorology," Henry continued in his 1848 report,

> it is proposed to employ, as far as our funds permit, the magnetic telegraph in the investigation of atmospheric phenomena. By this means, not only notice of the approach of a storm may be given to distant observers, but also attention may be directed to particular phenomena, which can only be properly studied by the simultaneous observations of persons widely separated from each other. For example, the several phases presented by a thunderstorm, or by the aurora borealis, may be telegraphed to a distance, and the synchronous appearances compared and recorded in stations far removed from each other. Also, by the same means, a single observatory . . . may give notice to all persons along the telegraph lines, of the occurrence of interesting phenomena.

Knowledge of an approaching storm, he thought, could be of great advantage to agriculture and commerce, and this, he concluded, "is a subject deserving the attention of the general government." The American meteorologist Cleveland Abbe, writing in the *American Journal of Science* in 1871, gave credit where credit was due: "The Smithsonian Institution first in the world organized a comprehensive system of telegraphic meteorology."

By 1857, a series of weather reports covering the area from New Orleans to New York and as far west as Cincinnati was coming in via the National Telegraph line. These reports were first published in the *Washington Evening Star*. The next year, a daily weather map, compiled from telegraphic reports received at ten o'clock every morning, was exhibited in the Smithsonian Building. This project combined in a practical way the telegraph and the work of the weather observers stationed throughout the country.

The fast-accumulating weather data, however, were soon put to strictly scientific uses. Voluminous reports, maps, tables, and charts were prepared and published on all phases of the work—rainfall, snowfall, temperatures, barometric pressure, storms, meteors, auroras, and other phenomena. Between 1852 and 1884, four editions of a *Collection of Meteorological Tables,* compiled by Professor Guyot and later expanded into the *Smithsonian Meteorological Tables,* were issued, and there were many other important scientific fruits of the project. Although the Civil War and the disastrous fire in the Smithsonian Building in 1865 interrupted the work, it did not end the cooperative spirit that the enterprise had engendered. In 1864, the North American Telegraphic Association, covering the entire United States and Canada, contributed the free use of all its lines for the scientific objective of the Institution.

In the meantime, however, agitation began for "a meteorological department under one comprehensive system with an adequate appropriation of funds." Henry, too, favored such a plan, and in 1869, when Congress established the Weather Bureau of the U.S. Signal Service, the Smithsonian's system of meteorological reports was turned over to the new bureau. Few new agencies of the federal government have ever had so firm a foundation. The venture represents one of the most successful experiments in cooperation that the Smithsonian ever attempted, and it served as an inspiration and pattern for many other undertakings. It had a more recent counterpart in the Moonwatch project of the Smithsonian's Astrophysical Observatory, in which, at the time of the launching of the first Russian *Sputnik,* on October 4, 1957, teams of voluntary observers were organized throughout the continent to assist in the visual tracking of artificial satellites.

The International Exchange Service, established in 1849, will be treated in detail in Chapter VIII, as will the Institution's publication program, begun in 1848 with the publication of the classic monograph *Ancient Monuments of the Mississippi Valley,* the first volume of the Smithsonian Contributions to Knowledge series. Suffice it to say here that Henry envisioned these projects as the best means he could devise to carry out that part of Smithson's prescription for the diffusion of knowledge. Since that time, other means have augmented the attempts to propagate the gospel of science and the arts *per orbem,* as the Smithsonian seal used to say.* But publication has always been the backbone of the Smithsonian's dissemination of information and has carried its name to every part of the globe.

Henry's attempt to keep the Smithsonian from being parochial was not always as successful as he wished. He wanted the activities of the Institution to be "for the benefit of all mankind," rather than to be geared too obviously for local consumption. But pressures from Congress and others to do something for the inhabitants of Washington, D.C., which at that time was not distinguished for its cultural opportunities, persuaded him to inaugurate a series of free

---

* The Smithsonian has been somewhat whimsical with respect to its corporate seal. Its first seal, adopted in 1847, carried a left-facing likeness of James Smithson and sufficed for forty-seven years. In 1893, Augustus St. Gaudens designed a new seal, which did very well for almost three-quarters of a century; it was sensible and traditional in design and carried the words "For the increase and diffusion of knowledge among men—*per orbem.*" In 1966, another seal began appearing on Smithsonian publications and documents; this consisted of the rather commonplace symbol of a sunburst, surrounded by "Smithsonian Institution, Washington, D.C." At one time I tried to talk the Secretary out of this latter infelicity with that ancient argument of Lucius Cary (Viscount Falkland) contained in his *Discourse on the Infallibility of the Church of Rome,* that "when it is not necessary to change, it is necessary not to change," but more recent philosophies prevailed.

lectures, and these continued for many years. The new building had been provided with an ample lecture hall, which, after all, had to be used, and so Henry yielded to popular demand. He wrote in his 1852 annual report, "Public lectures have become one of the characteristics of the day, and next to the press tend, more than any other means of diffusing knowledge, to impress the public mind."

Henry was able, with Smithsonian prestige behind him, to acquire the best lecturers available. The Smithsonian lectures, given chiefly while Congress was in session, began in February 25, 1847, with a series delivered in Washington's Odd Fellows Hall by the Englishman William Scoresby, an Arctic explorer, on "The Construction and Use of the Rosse Telescope." Next came four talks on "Modern Athens" by Professor Adolphus Louis Koeppen of Denmark in Carusi's Hall. A course of six sessions on geology by Dr. Edward Hitchcock, president of Amherst College, followed—the first to be given in the Smithsonian Building. As facilities improved, the program was expanded; in 1850, during the last session of Congress, the lectures ranged from a single talk on Holland by the Reverend Dr. George W. Bethune to a course on "The Unity of the Plan of the Animal Creation" by Professor Louis Agassiz of Cambridge, Massachusetts. "Whatever may have been the effect of these lectures in the way of diffusing knowledge," commented Henry, "it is evident, from the character of the men by whom they were delivered, that they presented truths intended to elevate and improve the moral and intellectual condition of the hearers." The lecture room in the Smithsonian Building was entirely burned out by the fire of 1865 and was not reconstructed. Although the lecture craze never reappeared with quite the same fervor as in those halcyon days before radio, television, and cinema, the Smithsonian has conducted some lectures each year, always free to the public.

Henry inherited a conservatism regarding money matters

from his Scottish Presbyterian ancestors. He believed in paying as you go and spending less than your income. From the income of the Smithson bequest, though, there was barely enough to keep the building maintained and to pay meager salaries, and today, in an era of deficit spending and exaggerated budgets, it seems amazing that he accomplished so much. In his tenth annual report, issued in 1855, he itemized the payment of salaries to only seven persons: the Secretary, who received a salary of $3,500 per year; an assistant secretary, whose salary was $2,000 per year; a chief clerk; a bookkeeper; a janitor; a laborer; and a watchman—plus a small amount for "extra clerks."

One of Henry's eminent qualities was his ability to judge good people, and he succeeded in attracting able and loyal workers to help carry on his programs. Although he did not have a large staff, his enthusiasm for the Institution was infectious, and he was able to enlist many cooperators from around the country and the world to complement those few in Washington. He was a man of warm human understanding, yet withal he possessed a stern dignity and determination that commanded respect and loyalty. His reputation was at stake with his scientfic colleagues in making the new establishment succeed, and he could not afford to make personal blunders. He knew what he wanted and was straightforward and persevering in getting it. There was nothing indecisive about him, as illustrated by his experience with the first Smithsonian librarian, Charles Coffin Jewett, whose contributions to American librarianship were considerable, but who was, perhaps, overambitious in view of the Institution's limited funds.

Joseph A. Boromé, in his biography *Charles Coffin Jewett* (Chicago: American Library Association, 1951), summarized Jewett's achievements:

He . . . did much to raise librarianship in the estimation of his contemporaries by combining scholarship with bibliography.

At Washington he established and gave direction to the Smithsonian . . . library, which he built up . . . from several scattered volumes to a collection of more than 32,000 volumes. . . . the acceptance by Congress of his recommendations on the transmission of copyright application copies of books free of charge; his survey of library resources of the United States which, revised by another, remained an unrivaled source of information . . . and his efforts to insure the success of the 1853 convention . . . were all noteworthy accomplishments. . . . The Library of Congress card is the answer to the problem he sought to solve by his plan for centralized cataloging at the Smithsonian. . . . Likewise the idea of a union catalog in the nation's capital. . . . It was Jewett who established the dictionary arrangement for catalogs. . . . It was Jewett who broke the hold of the ledger system of recording loans by inaugurating the slip system. . . . He was one of the first librarians in America to propose the instituting of branch libraries, to survey the library resources of the land from primary materials, and to draft and employ principles of accurate bibliographical transcription. . . .

In 1855, a difference of opinion arose between Henry and Jewett over the administration of the library, chiefly concerning expenditures, for Jewett felt that he should spend on the library all that the law allowed. They also differed over whether the library should be developed along predominantly scientific or literary lines. Science and Henry prevailed, and Henry removed Jewett from office in the face of congressional opposition. The episode well illustrates Henry's knack for picking a competent and productive man, even if he had to fire him later. Jewett later became superintendent of the Boston Public Library.

Henry directed the Smithsonian for thirty-two years, until his death in 1878. He left an imprint on the Institution that has never been erased, and his shadow still broods over the old red-stone Smithsonian Building. He was America's first great organizer of science. Two months after he became

Secretary, he wrote to the president of Union College: "If my plan is adopted, I am confident the name of Smithson will become familiar to every part of the civilized world. If I cannot succeed in carrying out my plans—at least in a considerable degree, I shall withdraw from the Institution." He did not withdraw, and he did succeed.

HENRY'S SUCCESSOR: SPENCER FULLERTON BAIRD

Four years after the Institution's founding, Henry chose his first assistant secretary, Spencer Fullerton Baird. Baird came from Dickinson College at Carlisle, Pennsylvania, his native state, and was one of the most promising young biologists of the country. Henry needed someone to free him from the burden of organizing a museum and art gallery, supervising publications, managing the International Exchange Service, and promoting the program of exploration, particularly of the national resources of the West, that the Institution had undertaken. Baird came well recommended, and on July 5, 1850, the Board of Regents approved his appointment at a salary of $1,500; he was to be "assistant secretary to act as Keeper of the Cabinet," or, museum curator. Henry would rather have seen the museum separate from the Smithsonian, for he did not relish the idea of having to depend on annual government appropriations for Smithsonian activities. It would, he feared, "annually bring the Institution before Congress as a supplicant for government patronage, and ultimately subject it to political influence and control." He wanted the Institution to "mingle its operations as little as possible with those of the general government" and "to ask nothing from Congress except the safe-keeping of its funds." But when he realized that this freedom was not to be, he welcomed his new assistant, who relieved him in a field in which he felt incompetent.

Baird seized every opportunity to promote the museum

activities, and they grew by design, not by accident. Deservedly, he has been called the father of the U.S. National Museum. He was a consummate museum man, with broad basic training in the natural sciences. His idea of a natural-history museum was a place in which the visitor might gain a knowledge of the fauna and flora of his country and where the serious student could find ample comparative materials for his research. He went to great lengths to aid such students and correspond with scores of them. Some of them were even allowed to take up living quarters in the towers of the Smithsonian Building.

Baird was a prodigious worker. The responsibilities he shouldered, the projects he carried through, the activities he promoted, both in and out of the Institution, were staggering, particularly in view of the limited help he had. Even correspondence had to be done longhand. During the thirty-seven years he was associated with the Smithsonian, he directed the Institution's International Exchange Service and assumed general charge of Smithsonian publications. He took over the exploration program, for which the Institution became famous (in an 1854 report, Baird described twenty-six important explorations undertaken during the preceding two years, including six Pacific Railroad surveys), and prepared the reports of many of the expeditions, including three of the volumes of the monumental *Explorations and Surveys of a Railroad Route from the Mississippi River to the Pacific Ocean*. He was instrumental in founding the U.S. Fish Commission in 1871, the first conservation agency of the federal government, and he served as its commissioner for sixteen years in addition to his Smithsonian labors. In connection with the work of the commission, Baird helped establish the Woods Hole Laboratory for marine research at Woods Hole, Massachusetts. He promoted Smithsonian participation in international expositions, particularly the 1876 Centennial Exposition in Philadelphia. He also edited the 4-volume

Iconographic Encyclopaedia of Science, Literature, and Art for a New York publisher and wrote voluminously on his scientific specialities, birds, mammals, and reptiles. Over the years, he built the U.S. National Museum into one of the best of its kind in the world, particularly in natural history.

Baird's leadership of the Institution's exploration program merits special mention. Baird and his associates gave careful scientific study to the collections gathered by the exploring parties. It was Baird's task to organize the classification and study of the specimens brought back to Washington from all corners of the continent, and taxonomic literature abounds in the new genera and species of animals bearing Baird's name as original describer.

In effect, Baird became adviser to the government on matters of exploration. In one instance, this role turned out to be of national importance. In 1864, after the failure of the Atlantic cable, the Western Union Telegraph Company conceived a plan to construct a telegraph line to Europe via Alaska and Siberia. An exploring expedition to British Columbia, the Northwest Territories of Canada, and Alaska was organized, and, through Baird's influence, Robert Kennicott, a promising young naturalist with previous experience in Alaska, was put in charge of the scientific corps. Kennicott was accompanied by seven young men—Henry M. Bannister, Ferdinand Bischoff, William Healey Dall, Henry W. Elliott, G. W. Maynard, Charles Pease, and Joseph T. Rotkrock— several of whom later attained distinction as scientists. They were to make natural-history collections for the Smithsonian and the Chicago Academy of Sciences.

The expedition reached Alaska as planned, but in May, 1866, Kennicott died of a heart attack. Soon afterward, the trans-Atlantic cable was assured of success, and Western Union dropped the whole matter of an overland telegraph line. The survey party was disbanded. In their few months in the Far North, however, they had penetrated territory never before seen or traversed by white men.

Bannister, a member of the Kennicott party, returned to Washington in 1867. The purchase of Alaska from Russia was being hotly debated in Congress at the time, and Bannister proved to be one of the few persons in the capital possessing firsthand knowledge of the area. He and Baird were called into consultation by Secretary of State William Henry Seward and Senator Charles Sumner. They testified before the Senate committee holding hearings on the proposed purchase and were able to furnish information that must have been convincing. Ernest P. Walker described their part in No. 13 of the Smithsonian War Background Studies:

> Baird pointed out the wealth of furs, fish, and timber, and showed that gold and copper had been found in the Territory and that agricultural crops could be raised there. Apparently practically all the specific information regarding the value of the Territory, including the usefulness of Sitka Harbor as a base for naval vessels, was supplied either by the Smithsonian Institution or by men who had worked in Alaska under its auspices.

James Alton James, in his book *The First Scientific Exploration of Russian America and the Purchase of Alaska,* quotes Bannister:

> The annexation was ridiculed at that time but we could testify that the country was worth the price asked. Time has sufficiently proved that we were right and I can safely say that we did not overstate anything. . . . The project of the Western Union Telegraph Company of an overland telegraph across Bering Straits to Europe was a failure but its greatest result was the annexation of Alaska.

When Joseph Henry died, Baird deservedly succeeded him

as Secretary, but he outlived Henry by only nine years. Baird died on August 19, 1887, at the age of sixty-four, after a long period of overwork and heart strain. His death ended the first four decades of Smithsonian history.

GEORGE BROWN GOODE AND THE U.S. NATIONAL MUSEUM

Another man who shaped the course of the National Museum, George Brown Goode, became the leading museologist of the country. He was a graduate of Wesleyan University and a Harvard student of Louis Agassiz. He and Baird first became acquainted in 1872. Goode was then only twenty-one, but Baird recognized the genuine potentialities in the young zoologist and, the following year, invited him to participate in the work of the U.S. Fish Commission, which was then beginning to take shape under Baird's organizing genius. Thus Goode began several years' volunteer service for the commission, during which he collected fishes along the eastern coast, wrote papers on what he was learning about them, and became not only a specialist in technical ichthyology but also a student of the economic problems relating to fisheries and the fishing industry. Upon Baird's invitation, he spent the winter of 1873 in Washington arranging fish specimens at the Smithsonian. There he met Secretary Henry and partook of the Henrys' hospitality and encouragement.

Although Goode kept his official connection with Wesleyan University until 1877, the Fish Commission and the Smithsonian gradually claimed him. He was given the title of curator of the museum. This was the beginning of two decades of unremitting hard work for the Institution, to which he became singularly devoted.

Baird and Goode together organized and executed the Smithsonian and Fish Commission exhibits at the Philadelphia Centennial Exposition in 1876. This experience set Goode off seriously into the realm of museum administration and organization. He was given a free hand in developing the exhibits in the new museum building, completed in 1881. A national museum, Goode believed, should serve a three-fold function: it should be a museum of record in which is preserved, as he wrote, "the material foundation of an enormous amount of scientific knowledge"; it should be a museum of research "which aims to make its contents serve in the highest degree as a stimulus to inquiry and a foundation for scientific investigation"; and it should be an educational museum "through its policy of illustrating, by specimens, every kind of natural object and every manifestation of human thought and activity." In the U.S. National Museum, he upheld this ideal. Though museum exhibition techniques and methods have changed considerably since Goode's day, and goals and principles of museums remain the same. The program still reflects his stated aims: "research, record, and the dissemination of knowledge."

Although Goode kept up with his scientific work to a remarkable degree and published many technical papers on ichthyology, as well as one popular book on American fishes, a voluminous genealogy of the Goode family, and several weighty bibliographies, he is ultimately remembered more as a historian and organizer of science than as a scientist. His forte was as a synthesizer of science. He was one of the first historians of American science, and his essays on the history of museums and the beginnings of natural history and science in America are still recognized as fundamental.

In January, 1887, a few months before the death of Secretary Baird, Goode was made an assistant secretary of the Institution. There began for him a prolifically productive period, but the burden became more than one man could bear, and he broke under the physical strain. He died at his Washington home on September 6, 1896, at the age of forty-five. As the magazine *Science* said at the time, he was "one of the ablest and best men in America."

During the time of Baird and Goode, there came to the museum a number of leaders of American natural history. They have been called the "Bairdians," a school characterized by exactitude in scientific statement, conciseness in deduction, and careful analysis of data, in contrast to many of the older European naturalists whose statements often had to be taken without benefit of documentary substantiation. Among the Bairdians was Elliott Coues, a brilliant ornithologist who worked chiefly on a collaborating basis and, with Thomas M. Brewer and Baird, helped to produce the outstanding *History of North American Birds.* Alone, he produced numerous and voluminous works on exploration and natural science. There was also William Healey Dall, an early Alaska explorer who served many years with the U.S. Geological Survey and was for fifty-nine years honorary curator of the Division of Mollusks and Tertiary Fossils in the museum. He contributed in many ways to the museum's scientific work in conchology and became the biographer of Baird. There was also William Henry Holmes, geologist, archeologist, and artist, and Leonhard Stejneger, the Norwegian-born biologist who spent a lifetime at the Smithsonian and distinguished himself both as an ornithologist and as a herpetologist. Another member was Robert Ridgway, who served for fifty-five years as the Smithsonian's chief ornithologist. His great work, which is probably the most ambitious undertaking in American systematic ornithology, was the multivolume *The Birds of North and Middle America,* a catalogue that included technical descriptions of every known form of bird from the northern section of the Western Hemisphere, with complete synonymies, identification keys, ranges, seasonal plumages, diagnostic characters, and measurements. The compilation of this work consumed most of his official time during the last thirty-five years of his life. Eight volumes were published by the Smithsonian during his lifetime and two appeared posthumously. After his death, the series was continued by

Dr. Herbert Friedmann, his successor as the museum's curator of ornithology. Ridgway also pioneered in the standardization of colors, and his classic work *Color Standards and Color Nomenclature* was widely used not only by naturalists but also by those in industry and the arts.

Any institution might well be proud to claim such dedicated, productive, scientific talent. To quote an ancient source, "There were giants in the earth in those days."

III

The Continuum

It is perhaps a truism to say that an organization is no stronger than the people who compose it. Buildings do not make an institution. Money will not buy ideas or bring devotion to an ideal. The Smithsonian is an ideal, and the men and women who have served it are what has made it great. It has attracted keen minds and extraordinary talent, sometimes genius, in an everchanging continuum. This is not to say that the Smithsonian has not had its share of misfits and incompetents, but the percentage of gem-quality rocks has been high. Many an unsung hero of science, an ivory-tower scholar world-renowned in his field, or an underpaid curator of philately, Copepoda, cryptogams, Bryozoa, airplane engines, or whatnot, has spent his life working at the Smithsonian. Of such has been comprised the hard core of personnel that has given the Smithsonian stability and accomplishment.

It would require several volumes to tell the stories of even the most illustrious of the men and women who have over the years formed the fabric of the Smithsonian and who have given life and luster to the Institution. A few have been mentioned, but there remain several others who must not be omitted—particularly the six Secretaries who followed Henry and Baird. Each has added his peculiar talents to the Smithsonian's development. Each has had an opportunity to shape the Institution's policies and to lead it in new directions.

SAMUEL PIERPONT LANGLEY: ASTROPHYSICS AND FLYING MACHINES

When Baird died in 1887, either of two assistant secretaries might have succeeded him. The choice, however, was in favor of a physical scientist rather than another biologist, and the post went to the astronomer Samuel Pierpont Langley. Langley had come to the Smithsonian the previous January after twenty years in Pittsburgh, where he had achieved a high reputation as director of the Allegheny Observatory and professor of astronomy and physics at the Western University of Pennsylvania (now the University of Pittsburgh).

A native of Roxbury, Massachusetts, and a descendant of New England first families, Langley was, following high school, largely self-educated. He was, in fact, endowed with a degree of mechanical genius that somehow managed to develop without benefit of college training. Astronomy became his consuming interest, and by the time he was thirty, after dabbling for seven years in architecture, he began to hold academic positions and could be called a professional astronomer. At fifty-three, when he came to the Smithsonian, his reputation, national and international, as a scientist, an inventor, and a writer of unusual ability was well established. He had already turned his attention to what he called the "new astronomy," which today we know as astrophysics, and had invented an extremely delicate instrument for measuring radiant energy, the bolometer, which opened up new vistas in the study of the solar spectrum. He studied sunspots and explored and located completely new portions of the infrared spectrum. This was pioneering research, and it was a great feather in the Smithsonian's cap when so eminent a man as Langley accepted the Secretaryship.

One of the enduring achievements of Langley's nineteen years as Secretary was the establishment of the Smithsonian

Astrophysical Observatory, which has been doing important research in astrophysics for about eighty years. It was under his administration also that the National Zoological Park was established and that the National Collection of Fine Arts, then called the National Gallery of Art, was given official status under the Smithsonian. He also promoted the compilation of the multivolume *International Catalogue of Scientific Literature,* an ambitious undertaking that was to be nurtured by the Smithsonian for nearly three decades until, because of lack of funds and of the impossibility of keeping up with the geometric progression of scientific literature, the project expired.

But it was Langley's experiments in aeronautics that brought him and the Smithsonian unprecedented prominence during the last ten years of his life. His interest in aviation was well developed before he came to the Smithsonian, for he had begun studies of flight while still at the Allegheny Observatory. With ingenious automatic instruments, he explored the lift and resistance of rapidly moving surfaces in the air and gradually developed his theories. In 1891, the Smithsonian published his monograph *Experiments in Aerodynamics.* Two years later, his study *The Internal Work of the Wind* appeared, based in part on his observations of the soaring of birds. He was determined to put the "art of aerodromics" on a scientific basis and, if possible, release it from the realm of quackery and impracticability with which most people at that time associated it.

Langley then began to build flying machines in the hope of demonstrating the truth of his theories. He studied engines and fuels and with model planes tested the experiments of other American and European inventors. Finally, he perfected his so-called Model No. 5, a 13-foot steam-powered "aerodrome" weighing only twenty-six pounds. On May 6, 1896, in the presence of Alexander Graham Bell and several other friends, Langley catapulted this model flying machine into the air from a houseboat on the Potomac River. When the engine stopped and the machine had landed safely on the water, it had flown about half a mile.

Six months later, Langley completed a larger model, No. 6, and on November 28, 1896, this machine made a successful flight of three-quarters of a mile in 105 seconds. These two flights greatly exceeded the work of previous experimenters and proved conclusively the practicability of sustained mechanical flight with a device heavier than air, unmanned but inherently stable. In 1897, in announcing the supposed conclusion of these experiments, Langley said:

> I have brought to a close the portion of the work which seemed to be specially mine—the demonstration of the practicability of mechanical flight—and for the next stage, which is the commercial and practical development of the idea, it is probable that the world may look to others. The world, indeed, will be supine if it do not realize that a new possibility has come to it, and that the great universal highway overhead is now soon to be opened.

His prophecy was true, but he had not yet finished his work. A great deal of public interest had been aroused, and, with the advent of the Spanish-American War, the government, too, began to take notice. President William McKinley, perhaps mindful of the fact that balloons had been successfully used in the Civil War, became interested in the potential of flight. Early in 1898, a board of U.S. Army and Navy officers was appointed to investigate Langley's experiments and to determine "what the possibilities were of developing a large-size man-carrying machine for war purposes." Their report was favorable, and the Board of Ordnance and Fortification of the War Department allotted $50,000 to Langley to develop, construct, and test a large aerodrome. The Smithsonian added $20,000 to aid the project.

When work on the machine began, Langley and his engineer, Charles M. Manly, were confronted with one difficulty after another. But their chief problem was to obtain an engine that met their exacting specifications. They visited builders of automobile engines in Europe but found no one who believed it possible to build an engine of the necessary power and the required light weight. They returned to the United States, and Manly set to work in the Smithsonian shops to construct the engine himself. He built a 5-cylinder, 52-horsepower, water-cooled gasoline engine weighing less than three pounds to the horsepower. It incorporated parts and certain valuable features of design from a rotary engine by Stephen M. Balzer, built under contract and purchased by the Institution.

On October 7, 1903, after many delays, with Manly in the aviator's seat and members of the Board of Ordnance watching, the machine glided down the launching track, only to plunge into the Potomac under the full power of the engine. It was agreed that the machine had not been properly released into the air and that the front guy post had caught in the launching gear. Little damage was done, and Manly was un-injured. The plane was repaired, some slight defects were corrected, and two months later another attempt was made, but with no better success. The machine again plunged into the river. The official report of the Board of Ordnance and Fortification attributed both failures to the launching device.

But whatever the trouble, these attempts were the virtual end of Langley's aeronautical experiments. The press and the public were merciless in their criticism. They had little of the faith that some of the scientists and inventors had shown and were more convinced than ever that human flight was and always would be impossible. Columnists and cartoonists the country over let loose. The Smithsonian and the government came in for their full share of the ridicule. The War Department withdrew its support. "Langley's Folly" appeared to be a closed incident. Yet only nine days after Langley's aircraft had "slid into the water like a handful of mortar," the Wright brothers at Kitty Hawk flew their heavier-than-air machine a little over 100 feet, with a man aboard.

For the Smithsonian, and indeed for the government, there was to be an important result from Langley's work. In 1913, the Smithsonian Board of Regents, in a spurt of foresight, decided to reopen Langley's aerodynamical laboratory; "to appoint an Advisory Committee; to add, as means are provided, other laboratories and agencies; to group them into a bureau organization; and to secure the cooperation with them of the Government and other agencies." The purpose of the laboratory was to be the study of the problems of aerodynamics, with such research and experimentation as might be necessary to increase the safety and effectiveness of aerial locomotion for the purposes of commerce, national defense, and the welfare of man. A committee was appointed, but soon thereafter, for legal reasons, it was discontinued. Together with the plans for the laboratory, however, it was the real forerunner of the National Advisory Committee for Aeronautics, which in 1958 was swallowed up by the behemoth now known as the National Aeronautics and Space Administration (NASA).

Langley died on February 27, 1906. The monumental record of his aeronautical contributions, *Langley Memoir on Mechanical Flight*, was published by the Institution five years later.

CHARLES DOOLITTLE WALCOTT: ACCOMPLISHMENTS AND CONTROVERSY

It was again the job of the Board of Regents to scour the field for a new Secretary, and it was nearly a year before an appointment was made. Several candidates were considered, including Henry Fairfield Osborn, curator of vertebrate paleontology at the American Museum of Natural History, who turned the offer down. The post passed to a natural scientist,

Charles Doolittle Walcott, who was appointed on January 23, 1907. He had succeeded John Wesley Powell as director of the U.S. Geological Survey in 1894, was well known as a paleontologist and geological explorer, and knew his way around in congressional and other government circles. Born in upstate New York on March 31, 1850, Walcott, like Langley, had struggled through life without benefit of a college degree. He was trained in Utica schools and under the scientific tutelage of James Hall, New York State geologist. He joined the Geological Survey at the age of twenty-nine, and his rapid upward climb read like a success story. His first official connection with the Smithsonian came in 1883 with his appointment as honorary curator in the National Museum's Department of Invertebrate Fossils. This position was complementary to his work as Geological Survey paleontologist. He had a room in the southwest corner of the old National Museum building, where he spent many hours with his fossils, arranging and identifying the museum's collections in paleontology and writing reports that appeared in the leading geological journals of the country.

Walcott did not give up his geology when he became Secretary but continued to carry on his researches. He spent nearly every summer in the Canadian Rockies studying Cambrian and pre-Cambrian formations—his specialty was the trilobites —and he made large collections of invertebrate fossils for the National Museum. The many publications that resulted from these studies won him wide recognition. To his office he brought considerable prestige. He became a trusted adviser to Presidents and lawmakers. He exercised an effective influence on the development of reclamation and forestry agencies in the government. Even as Secretary, his "extracurricular" activities were many. He was a moving spirit in the organization of the Carnegie Institution of Washington and of the Washington Academy of Sciences. He served as president of the National Academy of Sciences for six years and as president of the

American Association for the Advancement of Science for one term. At the Smithsonian, he promoted aviation and helped to organize the National Advisory Committee for Aeronautics, on which he served as chairman of the executive committee for several years. During his administration, the National Collection of Fine Arts was made a separate branch of the Institution, and the Freer Gallery of Art was added.

Walcott had a deep admiration for his predecessor, Langley. His lasting faith in Langley's aeronautical experiments led in a way to the famous but unfortunate Smithsonian-Wright controversy, which took many years to resolve.

In 1914, about ten years after the failure of the Langley plane, it was suggested to Walcott that the Langley plane be reconstructed according to original specifications and given a chance to vindicate its inventor. Many years later, Secretary Charles G. Abbot, Walcott's successor, meticulously described what happened in a paper entitled "The 1914 Tests of the Langley 'Aerodrome' ":

In March 1914, Secretary Walcott contracted with Glenn H. Curtiss to attempt a flight with the Langley machine. This action seems ill considered and open to criticism. For in January 1914, the United States Court of Appeals, Second Circuit, had handed down a decision recognizing the Wrights as "pioneers in the practical art of flying with heavier-than-air machines" and pronouncing Glenn H. Curtiss an infringer of their patent. Hence, in view of probable further litigation, the Wrights stood to lose in fame and revenue and Curtiss stood to gain pecuniarily, should the experiments at Hammondsport indicate that Langley's plane was capable of sustained flight in 1903, previous to the successful flights made December 17, 1903, by the Wrights at Kitty Hawk, N.C.

The machine was shipped to Hammondsport, N.Y., in April. Dr. A. F. Zahm, the Recorder of the Langley Aerodynamical Laboratory and expert witness for Curtiss in the patent litigation, was at Hammondsport as official representative of the

Smithsonian Institution during the time the machine was being reconstructed and tested. In the reconstruction the machine was changed from what it was in 1903 in a number of particulars. . . . On the 28th of May and the 2d of June, 1914, attempts to fly were made. After acquiring speed by running on hydroplane floats on the surface of Lake Keuka the machine lifted into the air several different times. The longest time off the water with the Langley motor was approximately five seconds. Dr. Zahm stated that "it was apparent that owing to the great weight which had been given to the structure by adding the floats it was necessary to increase the propeller thrust." So no further attempts were made to fly with the Langley 52 HP engine.

The Smithsonian, however, published statements to the effect that the 1914 experiment had shown that Langley's plane of 1903, without essential modification, was the first heavier-than-air machine capable of maintaining sustained human flight. When the restored Langley plane was first placed on exhibit in the National Museum on January 15, 1918, it bore this label: "The Original, Full-size Langley Flying Machine, 1903." Later, another label was substituted containing the claim that Langley's machine was "the first man-carrying aeroplane in the history of the world capable of sustained free flight," and, still later, this statement was modified by including the words "in the opinion of many competent to judge." These statements met with the disapproval and resentment of Orville Wright (Wilbur had died in 1912) and caused him, in 1928, to send his original Kitty Hawk machine "in exile" to the Science Museum at South Kensington, England, instead of to the Smithsonian Institution.

As long as Walcott was Secretary, this unfortunate Smithsonian-Wright controversy remained uncomposed and flared up perennially. However, Secretary Abbot, convinced that the Institution had been in the wrong and that his predecessor had acted unwisely in the matter, concluded his paper with a statement of correction and apology:

> If the publication of this paper should clear the way for Dr. Wright to bring back to America the Kitty Hawk machine to which all the world awards first place, it will be a source of profound and enduring gratification to his countrymen everywhere. Should he decide to deposit the plane in the United States National Museum, it would be given the highest place of honor, which is its due.

Orville Wright expressed satisfaction with the Smithsonian's stand, but when he died on January 30, 1948, his plane was still in England. Nevertheless, the executors of his estate agreed that it had been Orville's intention that the plane should ultimately be returned to the United States, and arrangements were finally concluded for its deposit in the National Museum. It was put on exhibit on December 17, 1948—the forty-fifth anniversary of the Wright brothers' flight.

As Secretary of the Smithsonian, Walcott was persuasive in getting financial support not only from Congress but also from private sources. In his memoir of Walcott, Abbot wrote of Walcott's effective ways with congressmen:

> From long and varied experience he drew wisdom for every emergency. . . . He knew men and how to deal with them. I attended him once at a Congressional sub-committee, when, as he was leaving, a prominent representative said to me that he thought government should not support science except for fully developed utility. As I was arguing the contrary, my chief casually interrupted with what seemed a complete change of subject. The Congressman was interested and Walcott led him on, until, in a moment, my antagonist was facing the proposition that a research which had been begun with no thought of utility five years before, now saved the government millions. As we drove away, I ventured to express my admira-

tion of his adroitness. Dr. Walcott replied, "These lawyers can beat you in argument, but they can't beat plain facts."

During the twenty years Walcott was Secretary, several large bequests came to the Institution. In fact, Walcott gave considerable sums to the Smithsonian, and when his wife, Mary Vaux Walcott, died in 1940, she bequeathed $400,000 to be added to the fund that Dr. Walcott and she had established for geological research and publication.

To the very end, Walcott was looking forward and planning great things for the Smithsonian. He organized a conference to discuss the future of the Institution, which was held on February 11, 1927, at which the President, the Vice-President, members of the Cabinet, and a group of the foremost American scientists and industrial leaders met under the chairmanship of Chief Justice William Howard Taft. It was the hope to promote a campaign to raise a $10 million endowment fund. Walcott was to have taken a leading part in the conference, but a short time before it was held, he suffered a stroke and died.

EARLY EXPERIMENTS IN ROCKETRY

What turned out to be a brilliant feather in the Smithsonian's hat during the Walcott years was the encouragement and financial help the Institution gave to Robert H. Goddard as early as 1915, at the beginning of his pioneering experiments with rockets. Both Walcott and Abbot saw the potential in Goddard's work at a time when he had nearly despaired of obtaining sufficient support to build and test his liquid-propellant rockets. Goddard's experiments were purely scientific, and no one could have foreseen the impact they would have on the world. In his biography of Goddard, Milton Lehman noted that the scientist once remarked about his first rocket, "All I'm trying to do is get this thing off the ground."

Though the grants to Goddard from the Smithsonian's limited Hodgkins Fund income were small when compared to today's research budgets and though he later obtained ampler support from other sources, particularly the Guggenheim Foundation, the Smithsonian assistance came at a critical time in his work. Two of Goddard's papers published by the Institution have now become collectors' items.

Dr. Wernher von Braun, the eminent rocket engineer and director of NASA's George C. Marshall Space Flight Center in Alabama, commented in a letter to me on the importance of Goddard's pioneering work:

> Dr. Goddard's "A Method of Reaching Extreme Altitudes," published by the Smithsonian Institution in 1919, is one of the fundamental works in theoretical rocketry. In it Dr. Goddard developed all of the equations of motion to show that the multi-stage rocket was the only vehicle capable of leaving the earth and operating in interplanetary space. While the existence of this monograph was not widely known in Europe during the 1920's, a few copies were available and were read with great interest by some rocket enthusiasts. In particular, Goddard sent one to Professor Hermann Oberth, who, with Goddard and Konstantin Tsiolkovsky, made modern rocketry and manned spaceflight possible through their early, pioneering works in the theory of rocketry.

CHARLES GREELEY ABBOT: THE SMITHSONIAN IN
DEPRESSION AND IN WAR

The man who succeeded Walcott, New Hampshire-born Charles Greeley Abbot, was a protégé of Langley and, like Langley, made his greatest contribution to the Smithsonian in the field of astrophysics. He came to the Institution in

1895, as an aide in the Astrophysical Observatory, directly on receiving his M.S. degree from the Massachusetts Institute of Technology. He rose to become director of the Observatory on Langley's death, assistant secretary of the Institution in 1918, and Secretary ten years later, a position he held until he retired in 1944, being the first Smithsonian Secretary not to die in office.*

Abbot's administration spanned difficult times—the Great Depression and World War II. Many of the Institution's investments were not productive, government appropriations and salaries were cut, and support for science dwindled. It was difficult, if not impossible, to obtain sufficient funds to carry on the work of the Institution. Still, Abbot left a record of scientific achievement for himself and definite growth for the Institution. For one thing, under the stimulus of Dr. William M. Mann, energetic director of the National Zoological Park, the federal Works Progress Administration (WPA) building program made funds available for some badly needed buildings at the zoo. At a total cost of $1.3 million, there were built a new reptile house, a wing on the bird house, a small mammal house, a central heating plant, and shops, which made the facilities at the National Zoo more nearly adequate and more attractive. In addition, several notable gifts came to the Institution. One of these was the large art collection of John Gellatly, valued at $4.5 million, which is now a part of the National Collection of Fine Arts. Another cultural bonanza was Andrew W. Mellon's gift that created the National Gallery of Art.

Abbot, unlike his predecessor, was never fond of administrative work but was happiest when carrying on his research at the Astrophysical Observatory in Washington, at Mount Wilson Observatory in California, and at other places throughout the world where solar investigations were in prog-

* On May 31, 1969, Charles Greeley Abbot celebrated his ninety-seventh birthday at his home in Hyattsville, Maryland.

ress. Like Langley, he was an ingenious instrument-maker and inventor. He developed, for example, the pyrheliometer, an instrument that measures in calories per square centimeter per minute the intensity of the sun's rays received at the earth's surface. About a hundred pyrheliometers were built at the Smithsonian and distributed at cost to observatories throughout the world.

Abbot worked out definite periodicities of solar variation that partially matched terrestrial temperature curves, a line of investigation for which he became famous and which occupied much of his time even after he retired as Secretary. His objective was to apply this information directly to long-range weather forecasting. In 1947, he announced the discovery of a "cosmic week"—a period of 6.6456 days that appeared in variations of the radiation output of the sun and in variations in temperature at three selected Weather Bureau stations. His findings were based on records of thirty-five years and were subjected to mathematical analysis. The cycle is remarkable, he found, because of its regularity pointing still more strongly to a close relationship between solar radiation and weather conditions on the earth. Although few other meteorologists accepted Abbot's theories of the relation of sunspots and solar radiation to weather, he never gave up trying to convince them.

In 1923 and 1924 Abbot devised an instrument to measure the heat of stellar spectra that was so sensitive as to be able to measure the heat of a match two thousand miles away if no atmosphere intervened. He measured the heat of ten of the brightest stars and afterward constructed a radiometer, using fly wings, ten times more sensitive than his previous instrument.

Other inventions included a solar heater that utilized the heat of the sun. In one model, liquid heated from the sun's rays reflected from mirrors was circulated through insulated tubes to a steam boiler, where steam was raised at 175 pounds pressure to the square inch, sufficient for one-half horsepower. Another model generated enough heat to bake bread and cook meat. As recently as 1968, Dr. Abbot's inventive genius was still very much alive. At the annual meeting of the National Academy of Sciences, he gave a paper on the subject "Electric Power from Sun's Rays," based on an invention he had just patented.

During World War II, Abbot promoted activities at the Institution that contributed to the war effort. He appointed a committee to canvass possible tasks the Smithsonian could undertake. One successful project was the publication of twenty-one War Background Studies, a series of illustrated booklets on the peoples, geography, history, natural history, and other features of the areas the war reached, especially in the Pacific. Another project was the preparation for the Navy of a manual, *Survival on Land and Sea,* which was widely distributed to the armed forces. The Smithsonian's emphasis during the war years was summed up in its 1945 annual report:

> A large part of the effort of the staff was diverted to work connected directly or indirectly with the war, and the Smithsonian Institution was found to be an essential cog in the great war machine in Washington. Although its role was inconspicuous as compared with those of the large war agencies, nevertheless it was found to offer services not readily available elsewhere—services whose lack might well have led to costly mistakes and delays.

Another wartime activity fostered by Abbot was the Ethnogeographic Board, a nongovernmental agency created cooperatively by the Smithsonian, the National Research Council, the American Council of Learned Societies, and the Social Science Research Council to act as a clearinghouse for anthropological and geographical information required by military agencies of the government. Staffed principally by

Smithsonian scientists, it proved exceedingly useful until the end of the war rendered it no longer necessary.

The Institute of Social Anthropology, an autonomous unit of the Bureau of American Ethnology, also began under Abbot's regime. Though this agency was relatively short lived (1943–52), it accomplished notable work in cooperative training in anthropological teaching and research with other American republics. One of its lasting monuments was the publication of a series of sixteen monographs in the field of social anthropology.

ALEXANDER WETMORE: HAPPIEST WITH BIRDS

With Abbot's resignation on June 30, 1944, the Secretaryship again passed, according to tradition, to a natural scientist, Alexander Wetmore. Wisconsin-born, Wetmore had been associated with the Institution since 1924, when for five months he had served as director of the National Zoological Park. Walcott then selected him to be his assistant secretary in charge of the U.S. National Museum, the largest of the Smithsonian's components.* By then, Wetmore was a well-seasoned biologist, following in the footsteps of Spencer Baird in his eminence as an ornithologist. He had served with the U.S. Biological Survey, had led an exploring expedition to the mid-Pacific, had spent a year studying migrant shorebirds in South America, and had published many

* Today, the name U.S. National Museum, as applied to a definite organizational entity, is passing into disuse. The expansion and diversification of all the Smithsonian's museum activities have favored the restructuring of the whole museum complex, with each museum set up as an independently administered unit rather than gathered under one directorship. In this book, however, written while this change was evolving, the name U.S. National Museum is frequently used in its historical sense. As a matter of fact, it will be used by outsiders probably for a long time to come, for the roots of more than a century are difficult to eradicate. But the reader should remember that what was once the U.S. National Museum is now two separate museums: the National Museum of Natural History and the National Museum of History and Technology.

scientific papers. In later years, he became a world authority on avian classification, fossil birds, and the birds of Panama. His selection from within the ranks was well deserved.

John K. Terres wrote of Wetmore in an article in a 1948 issue of *Audubon Magazine:*

> The quiet-spoken Wetmore is a striking figure, whether speaking before a scientific meeting, or collecting birds in the heart of a tropical forest. His tall, wiry frame is erect, his smooth white hair, close-cropped, his hazel eyes steady behind plain rimless glasses. About him there is an air of quiet modesty, but of hidden strength, emphasized by his clean-shaven jaw, wide firm mouth, and slightly uptilted nose. His deep, drawling voice and earnest manner command respect, and he seldom speaks at length unless he has something worth telling. Although he likes the company of men, particularly scientists, he is happiest when he is with birds.

This passage describes him as well today, at the age of 83, as it did when it was written, twenty years ago.

Wetmore carried on assiduously the policies of his predecessors Walcott and Abbot but faced problems of expansion, which somehow always outstripped the Smithsonian's appropriations and income. Administrative demands increased, and during the 1940's, two assistant secretaries were appointed— John E. Graf and John L. Keddy. The number of visitors to the various Smithsonian buildings crept upward until, by the end of Wetmore's incumbency, they totaled nearly 8.5 million annually. (By 1967, this figure had reached nearly 20 million.) Museum accessions increased in like proportion. In report after report to Congress, Wetmore drew attention to the "perennial pressures" and urgently pleaded for funds for additional personnel, increased housing, and expanded services and operations. This insistence finally began to be heard in Congress and served as the groundwork for greater things to come, many of which, unfortunately, did not arrive until Wetmore retired at the end of 1952, after twenty-eight years' service with the Institution.

During Wetmore's administration, two bureaus were added to the Smithsonian organization—the National Air Museum and the Canal Zone Biological Area, now called the Smithsonian Tropical Research Institute. Soon after he became Secretary, Wetmore entered into a cooperative program with the National Park Service known as the "river basin surveys." The program, which operated as an autonomous unit of the Bureau of American Ethnology, was designed to examine the extent and nature of archeological and paleontological remains occurring in areas to be flooded by the construction of dams by the Bureau of Reclamation and the U.S. Corps of Engineers. It was technically known as the Inter-Agency Archeological and Paleontological Salvage Program. The project turned out to be a long-term and very productive scientific venture, and, though recently relinquished to the National Park Service, it is still in progress today, after nearly a quarter of a century.

In 1946, Wetmore directed the celebration of the one-hundredth anniversary of the founding of the Smithsonian Institution with appropriate ceremonies and the issuance of a commemorative 3-cent U.S. postage stamp. However, the celebration was in low key because of exigencies in the wake of the ending of World War II.

As a scientist, Wetmore brought great distinction to the Smithsonian, as witnessed by the extramural positions that he held from time to time—notably, president of the Tenth International Ornithological Congress, home secretary of the National Academy of Sciences, secretary-general of the Eighth American Scientific Congress, chairman of the Inter-departmental Committee on Research and Development, and trustee of the National Geographic Society.

LEONARD CARMICHAEL: A DECADE OF EXPANSION

To fill Wetmore's place, the Board of Regents for the first time went outside the Institution for a Secretary. Their choice was Leonard Carmichael, one of America's leading psychologists. Carmichael, born in Germantown, Pennsylvania, in 1898, had had many years' experience in academic administration, was thoroughly familiar with scientific disciplines, and was a forceful promoter, writer, and speaker. When he took office on January 1, 1953, he had been president of Tufts College for fourteen years and had served as director of that institution's laboratories of sensory psychology and physiology. He had formerly been a faculty member at Brown and Princeton universities and dean at the University of Rochester. As a physiological psychologist, he had published papers on such topics as the origin and development of behavior in relation to the functions of the sense organs, and he was the author of a standard manual of child psychology. During World War II, he had held numerous posts in Washington, including the directorship of the National Roster of Scientific and Specialized Personnel.

Leaving the strictly academic life, Carmichael found the Smithsonian's academicism of a somewhat different stripe. He found not a community of classroom professors and scholars geared to the intellectual needs of young America but a community of experts in numerous branches of natural and unnatural history—taxonomists, curators, historians of the arts and sciences, archeologists, astronomers, taxidermists, technicians, editors, librarians—all working in their highly specialized cubicles of learning toward the achievement of James Smithson's rather vague objective—the increase and diffusion of knowledge among men. To be sure, the Smithsonian had its parallels to a great university in its concern with research and with publication and education in the broadest sense.

Carmichael possessed a salutary historical perspective, an instinct for seeing how things might be improved, for sensing the urgency of action to solve pressing problems. At the same time, he had an appreciation of the reservoir of Smithsonian history, of the reasons why, through its more than a century of service, it had won a special place in the hearts of American citizens as well as a high reputation throughout the world. He did not believe that the embers of the past should be extinguished for the sake of novelty. He was an admirer of Alexander Pope and a conservative at heart.

Still, there were things to be done. In his first annual report, issued in 1953, Carmichael wrote:

> The Smithsonian is not an "inflated agency," but rather one that in recent decades has not been permitted to perform for the citizens of this country its many basic functions as well as it would have been able to do if it had been given more financial support. During this time, however, the loyal but numerically declining staff of the Institution has carried on approximately 150 percent more work than was required of their more numerous predecessors.

The complaint was not new. It was the same song that Wetmore, Abbot, Walcott, and Langley had sung, but the time was now ripe. The longtime arguments for new exhibit halls, new buildings, and more personnel began to pay off. Financial support from Congress increased, a program was approved for the modernization and rehabilitation of the Smithsonian's museum exhibits, and plans for new buildings were approved and inaugurated. By the time Carmichael's regime came to a close in 1964, he had seen this program marvelously advanced and could point, as he did in his 1963 annual report, to a decade of enviable accomplishments. Among these, the new buildings, particularly the Museum of History and Technology and the new wings to the Natural History Building, received prime emphasis, but research, personnel improvement and expansion, and publication had by no means been neglected.

Perhaps the most spectacular organizational move made during the Carmichael years was the restructuring of the Smithsonian Astrophysical Observatory and the removal of its headquarters from Washington, D.C., to Cambridge, Massachusetts. A collaborative working agreement was arranged with the Harvard College Observatory, Dr. Fred L. Whipple was made the new director on the retirement of Loyal B. Aldrich, and the work of the observatory took on new directions. How all this came about is related by Bessie Z. Jones in her history of the observatory, *Lighthouse of the Skies*. Suffice it to say here that the move was another indication of the Smithsonian's growing desire to identify itself more closely with the academic world, to involve itself to a greater degree in the excitement and immediacy of the new "age of science," and to take longer looks into the future.

S. Dillon Ripley: A New Museum and a Two-hundredth Anniversary

The eighth Secretary, S. Dillon Ripley, appointed to succeed Carmichael after his 11-year term, took office on February 1, 1964, only a few days after the Museum of History and Technology had been dedicated by President Lyndon B. Johnson and opened to the public. Proceeding cautiously at first, Ripley soon moved into high gear, made drastic organizational changes, brought new blood into the staff, eased out dead wood, inaugurated new programs, and experimented in many new directions. Particularly, as he outlined in his first annual report, he proposed to develop programs in cooperation with universities to reassert, in the words of Joseph

Henry, the Smithsonian's "leadership in education and scholarship in America," to broaden the Institution's traditional cooperation with museums throughout the world, to strengthen the Institution's research programs, especially in some areas of the natural sciences, and to extend its international activities beyond traditional overseas field expeditions and research by cooperation with other government agencies and private institutions in exchange programs involving both personnel and exhibits.

Before coming to the Smithsonian, Ripley had been professor of biology at Yale University and director of the university's Peabody Museum of Natural History. He had also served on the staffs of the Academy of Natural Sciences of Philadelphia, the American Museum of Natural History, and, for a short time, the U.S. National Museum. He was trained as a biologist, his particular love being ornithology. He had traveled widely and conducted expeditions to such places as New Guinea and had become something of an authority on the birds of Asia. He was active as a conservationist. At his home in Litchfield, Connecticut, he operated, as a hobby, a considerable aviary. When he became Secretary, Ripley conveyed the impression that he meant business and that those who did not like it could jolly well pack their bags. Some of them did. He was friendly but firm and determined.

The year after Ripley became Secretary the Institution celebrated the two-hundredth anniversary of the birth of James Smithson. This event gave the Institution an opportunity at a natural turning point in its history to take stock of itself and advertise itself to the world. The celebration took the form of an international meeting in Washington, at which, for three days in September, several hundred invited scientists and scholars were entertained, banqueted, and provided the opportunity to see the President of the United States and to hear addresses by such eminent thinkers as Robert Oppenheimer, Lewis Mumford, Sir Kenneth Clark, Arthur Koestler, and Claude Lévi-Strauss, among others. At the end, it was pretty well agreed that the Smithsonian could put on a good party, and that, if this were any sign, a new day for the Institution had dawned.

Indeed, the celebration lent a certain carnival air to the Mall that has never gone away. Band concerts, chamber music from the Smithsonian tower, carrousels, kite-flying, balloon flights, barbershop quartet singing, and other divertissements, all in the open air, became the order of the day, often under the joint aegis of the Smithsonian and the National Park Service.

But the new image created by Ripley, although not universally admired, may go deeper than appearances. He has made his greatest contribution so far in his emphasis on the role that museums can exert in our changing culture. He believes that too few people today realize the potential educational use of museums, art galleries, and kindred institutions, which can be a real force on the urban educational scene. He thinks that people do not realize how vital the open forms of education are to all ages, how many persons are involved in these cultural institutions, either in research or in the production of exhibits. Museums of art, he believes, should be friendly places and thus should be an important influence in fostering man's understanding of his inward self. Natural-history museums should lead to a realization that, in spite of man's attempts to engineer his environment, certain patterns, such as the annual migration of birds, persist in nature, apparently outside of man's control. Thus, natural-history museums play a useful role in showing man as part of an ecosystem.

Future museums, be believes, must diversify their product and their appeal and take an active part in education. Man's social and intellectual growth is too closely linked with a need to develop taste and an aesthetic sense to allow art appreciation to be insulated from general comprehension, from open education. Our needs are far too great to allow us to create artificially separate realms of the arts, the humanities, the sciences.

More will be said about some of the programs initiated since 1964 and about the prospects for the future of the Smithsonian. Here the prime emphasis has been on the men who have directed and done the work, what they have accomplished, and something of the circumstances and philosophy behind their actions. It would be fine if there were space to give accounts of more of the Smithsonian personnel, past and present—men like Aleš Hrdlička, the internationally known physical anthropologist; Cyrus Adler, the distinguished Orientalist; the adventurous John Wesley Powell, founder of the Bureau of American Ethnology; and Gerrit S. Miller, Jr., a mammalogist who first suspected the fraudulence of Piltdown Man. There are hundreds of important men and women who have added and are adding their own particular warp and woof to the Smithsonian fabric. It is after all the people who do the work that make an organization— and the Smithsonian has attracted an unusual number of good ones.

But it is time now to turn to the structure they created and the functions that evolved under their direction.

IV

"The Smithsonian Is Not a Museum"

We tend to hold in awe the things we do not understand, and the Smithsonian Institution is no exception. The American people have put it on a pedestal; they praise it, but few fully understand it.

To a visitor in Washington, the Smithsonian is indeed bewildering. He is told that an old, red-stone, cathedral-like building is called the Smithsonian. He visits the sumptuous National Gallery of Art nearby and the Freer Gallery of Art and learns that these, too, are under the Smithsonian's protective wing. He tramps through the halls of various museums and sees the Smithsonian name everywhere. He drives out to the zoo in Rock Creek Park and discovers that the National Zoological Park is under Smithsonian direction. And, if he cares to inquire, he will learn that there are Smithsonian operations in New York City, Cambridge, Massachusetts, and the Canal Zone.

It is not difficult to describe the Smithsonian Institution, but it is almost impossible to define it. Like a Gothic cathedral, it is unconfined and never completed. It is greater than the sum of its parts.

Not surprisingly, the Smithsonian's complexity engenders

paradoxes and popular misconceptions. When I first joined the staff of the Institution in 1931, there was, at the front door of the Smithsonian Building, a visitors' sign—long since removed—that began with the words "The Smithsonian Institution is not a Museum." Perhaps psychologically such a negative statement was not the best way to dispel a misconception in the public's mind, but it had the effect, no doubt, of startling the visitor, and perhaps the sign should have remained, for even today in many minds the Smithsonian is but a place where one may see old airplanes and automobiles, stuffed animals, the Hope Diamond, the gowns of the Presidents' wives, and other miscellaneous curiosities.

The corpus of the Smithsonian today is made up of an aggregation of bureaus and near bureaus—museums, art galleries, and research offices and departments—that have collected under the protective skirts of the Institution in its century and a quarter of history. Some of them are totally governmental, some quasi-governmental, and some nongovernmental in status. Some are big, some small. Joseph Henry did not think much of having federally supported agencies attached to the Smithsonian and expressed this view candidly in his 1849 annual report: "It could not be the intention of Congress that an Institution founded by the liberality of a foreigner, and to which he has affixed his name, should be charged with the keeping of a separate museum, the property of the United States." But Henry was wrong. Congress did so intend, and Henry was unable to keep the Smithsonian pure. The bureaus proliferated, and gradually the principal activities of the Institution found their niches within these appendages. But in the last analysis, the bureaus are not the enduring soul of the Smithsonian. As Secretary Carmichael stated in *James Smithson and the Smithsonian Story*, "If—by any stretch of the imagination—its 'bureaus' should be translated to the moon, the Smithsonian's foundation would remain, and new fields of service and new ways to 'increase and diffuse knowledge' would arise like the phoenix bird. The old foundation is firm." *

GOVERNMENT AND MANAGEMENT

A recent handbook issued by the Institution states that "the Smithsonian Institution is an independent establishment devoted to public education, basic research, and national service in science, the humanities, and the arts." This program, of course, is but an extension of James Smithson's broad pattern and Joseph Henry's plan. Henry insisted that Smithson's bequest was "for the benefit of mankind," that the Institution "is not a national establishment, but the establishment of an individual," and that the U.S. Government had agreed to act as trustee for the bequest and "to carry out the design of the testator."

Strictly speaking, then, the Smithsonian is not a government agency, although this point has been argued from time to time. To be quite realistic about it, however, the Smithsonian today is part government and part nongovernment, a rather convenient arrangement. To carry out those functions assigned by the federal government, such as administration of the national museums and other bureaus or branches established by congressional authority, the Smithsonian receives appropriations from Congress. The Institution's other activities are financed from the income from its endowments, which began with Smithson's gift, or from other private sources. Several Smithsonian branches, such as the Freer Gallery of Art and the National Gallery of Art, were established through the beneficence of single individuals, with endowments restricted to the support of the particular agency.

---

* As a matter of fact, the trend today within the government as a whole is toward subduction of bureaus. In the behemoth Department of Agriculture, for example, none of the formerly numerous bureaus remain per se, and all functions and activities are now organized along program lines.

Thus the Smithsonian wears two hats. Though at times its position has led to some complexity and even confusion in administration, it affords a good deal of flexibility. In fact, the Smithsonian is not unlike Bert Leston Taylor's dinosaur, that "model beast" that

> . . . could reason *a priori*
> As well as *a posteriori.*
> If something slipped his forward mind
> 'Twas rescued by the one behind.

Over the years, this flexibility has stood the Smithsonian in good stead, for when Congress has seen fit to reject the Institution's requests and programs, it has sometimes been able to carry on with private funds, provided the project was not too big or beyond its means at the moment.

The composition of the statutory Board of Regents, the Institution's governing body, has been described in Chapter II. In addition to the regents, the original Act provided for an organizational superstructure made up of ex officio "members" of the Institution and known as the Establishment. This body is composed of the President of the United States, who serves as the presiding officer; the Vice-President; the Chief Justice; and the members of the President's Cabinet. In the early days of the Institution, the Establishment functioned in a supervisory way, but it gradually became a sort of vermiform appendix that today has virtually ceased to function, though no one has suggested its removal. During the first thirty years, the Establishment held only nine meetings. It met last on May 5, 1877, and adjourned to meet again at the call of the President, who has been content to let well enough alone. Legally, this body was given the authority by Congress to administer the Smithson trust, since the founders of the Smithsonian had determined that the federal government should not administer the Institution directly. For all practical purposes, however, the Establishment has delegated this authority to the Board of Regents.

The link between the now inactive Establishment and the Board of Regents lies in the Chief Justice and the Vice-President, both of whom are ex officio regents and one of whom traditionally has been named Chancellor of the Institution.

The Board of Regents holds at least one meeting a year. In recent years, it has met twice each year, once in January and again in May. At these sessions, the board receives annual and interim reports from the Secretary, reviews the activities of the Institution, approves the budget, outlines policies of administration and action, and passes on major personnel changes. The 3-man executive committee of the board acts in certain interim matters and serves as a sort of advisory committee to the Secretary.

A roster of the eminent men who have served on the Smithsonian Board of Regents—statesmen, scientists, scholars, businessmen—would be lengthy indeed. In the early days there were, for example, men such as Louis Agassiz, Alexander Dallas Bache, George Perkins Marsh, Jefferson Davis, Robert Dale Owen, James Dwight Dana, and Asa Gray. Later, such men as Alexander Graham Bell, John C. Merriam, Arthur H. Compton, and Vannevar Bush served as regents. As this book is written, the ex officio regents are Vice-President Spiro T. Agnew and Chief Justice Warren E. Burger; the three senatorial regents are Clinton P. Anderson of New Mexico, J. William Fulbright of Arkansas, and Hugh Scott of Pennsylvania; the regents from the House of Representatives are Frank T. Bow and Michael J. Kirwan, both of Ohio, and George H. Mahon of Texas; and the citizen regents are John Nicholas Brown, businessman of Providence, Rhode Island; William A. M. Burden, financier of New York; Crawford H. Greenewalt, scientist and industrialist of Wilmington, Delaware; Caryl P. Haskins, research scientist and president of the Carnegie Institution of Washington; and Thomas J. Watson,

Jr., corporation executive of Greenwich, Connecticut. In the last-named group there is at present a vacancy. There has never been a woman on the board; this is merely a statement of fact, not an inference.

The Smithsonian has always been relatively free of political pressures. Congressmen have found the Institution a poor place for patronage. To my knowledge, there have been very few persons who have obtained their jobs at the Smithsonian through political influence, and in cases where such pressure might have been successfully exerted, it is enough to give the employee in question a cloudy start. Even the Smithsonian Secretaryship is not a political plum. The Secretary is chosen and appointed by the Board of Regents, without benefit of the Civil Service Commission's advice, congressional action, or Presidential ratification. He serves an indefinite tenure, terminated only by resignation, death, or retirement (in recent years at age sixty-five). It is unthinkable that he or any of his subordinates would be removed from office for political reasons. In general, in selecting a Secretary—and there have been only eight—the regents have adhered to the principles contained in the resolution adopted by the committee delegated to select the first Secretary in 1846:

> *Resolved*: that it is essential, for the advancement of the proper interests of the trust, that the Secretary of the Smithsonian Institution be a man possessing weight of character and a high grade of talent; and that it is further desirable that he possess eminent scientific and general requirements; that he be a man capable of advancing science and promoting letters by original research and effort, well qualified to act as a respected channel of communication between the Institution and scientific and literary individuals and societies in this and foreign countries; and, in a word, a man worthy to represent, before the world of science and letters, the Institution over which this Board presides.

To some degree, these principles have trickled down to influence the selection of the rank and file at the Smithsonian, as well.

A MUSHROOMING ORGANIZATION

The contrast between the small and simple Smithsonian organization in Joseph Henry's day and the complex into which it has developed in the twentieth century is not merely a demonstration of Parkinson's Law; it is also an illustration of the growth of American institutions in general. Henry began with a few bare principles and plans. He knew that under the law he had to set up a museum, an art gallery, and a library, and these he conscientiously promoted. But at the same time, he did his utmost to establish the reputation of the Institution in research and exploration and in publication. The patterns that he laid down still persist through the Smithsonian fabric. But the lines have proliferated in many directions, until today there is virtually no branch of learning in which the Smithsonian is not involved in one way or another.

Though the original plan provided for activity in the humanities, Henry decided that the sciences should be the Institution's forte. Today, in contrast, the humanities are demanding an increasing role in Smithsonian programs, and recently an assistant secretary for History and Art was named to supervise the functions that fall into these departments of learning. This change reflects the expanding concepts of the Smithsonian's legitimate business as well as a general feeling throughout the nation that the humanities, following the scientific upsurge of recent decades, were being overlooked.

When Joseph Henry inaugurated his program for the Smithsonian, he sought to serve the whole nation, not just the District of Columbia, where the Smithsonian happened to be located. As the Institution developed, he enunciated a principle of action that has come to be called the coefficient of cooperation.

Hundreds of examples could be cited to demonstrate how Smithsonian programs, far from operating in a vacuum, interrelate with those not only of government agencies at many levels but also of the academic world, scientific societies, private enterprise, and individuals. One of the earliest such projects was Joseph Henry's cooperative program for gathering meteorological data. There were such enterprises as the Institution's exploration projects, beginning with Baird's western surveys, nearly every one of which required cooperative assistance from many individuals and public agencies; the Smithsonian-Chrysler African Expedition of 1926, which yielded the largest single collection of animals ever imported for the National Zoological Park; and several joint expeditions with the National Geographic Society, for which the Society usually furnished funds and the Smithsonian personnel. There was also the Eighth American Scientific Congress, held in Washington, D.C., in 1940, in which the Smithsonian cooperated with the Department of State by furnishing top leadership and assistance, and the river basin surveys, an interagency archeological program described elsewhere.

In addition, the Smithsonian has performed contract research for the Atomic Energy Commission, the National Aeronautics and Space Administration, and others; established the Moonwatch project of the Astrophysical Observatory; issued many publications under the Smithsonian imprint that were financed by other institutions and individuals; produced a 6-year nationwide radio series in cooperation with the Office of Education and the Works Progress Administration; lent assistance to the Federal Bureau of Investigation in identifying skeleton remains in crime investigations; and assisted in identification and documentation of museum materials for other institutions and individuals. The list could go on and on.

Throughout its history, the Smithsonian has had particularly close relationships with other scientific organizations. Henry helped, for example, to found the National Academy of Sciences. Smithsonian men have held high positions in the Academy, including the presidency, and all Smithsonian Secretaries have been members. The organization and programs of the Philosophical Society of Washington, the Anthropological Society of Washington, the Washington Academy of Sciences, and the American Association of Museums, to name but a few, have been fostered in one way or another by the Smithsonian. For forty years, the American Association for the Advancement of Science was provided office space in the Smithsonian Building. Such arrangements and relationships are of mutual benefit and serve to advance the cause of science in ways that the Smithsonian cannot undertake alone.

Fifty years after the founding of the Institution, Daniel Coit Gilman, then president of the Johns Hopkins University, summed up this phase of the Smithsonian's development in George Brown Goode's book *The Smithsonian Institution, 1846–1896:*

> The most important service which the Smithsonian Institution has rendered to the nation—intangible but none the less appreciable—has been its fifty years of constant cooperation with the government, with public institutions, and with individuals, in every enterprise, scientific or educational, which needed its advice, support, or aid from its manifold resources. Each secretary in his own way has been free, and has felt free, to open new roads and enter fresh fields when the public good required it and the funds at command permitted expansion.

The danger to be avoided has always been that of Stephen Leacock's character who jumped on his horse and rode off in all directions. Perhaps the Smithsonian has not always averted this danger, but the freedom of action inherent in the Institution's organization has always been there.

Henry, through his wide contacts with the world of learning, through his publication program, through his encouragement of research, and, to quote Gilman again, through "his friendly relations with every agency in the land devoted to the encouragement of learning," made the Smithsonian "the great auxiliary of science and education throughout the length and breadth of the land." If this reputation could be plotted on a curve, there would be ups and downs in the course of the Smithsonian's now nearly 125 years. But in general, it has been an upward curve.

In recent years, the Institution has undertaken many new and ambitious programs, particularly in an effort to identify the Smithsonian more closely with the academic world. For example, the Institution has sponsored cooperative projects with universities, offered graduate and postdoctoral fellowships, and opened its research opportunities to qualified students and specialists. The president of George Washington University, in his report on developments in the university during the year 1966, described several joint ventures:

> In cooperation with the Smithsonian Institution, a doctoral program in American Thought and Culture, with an emphasis on the material culture of the United States, was established. The United States National Museum joined with the [university's] Department of Biological Sciences in a program for doctoral candidates in invertebrate zoology. The Department of Geology added the doctoral field of petrology to its Smithsonian affiliations.

In his 1966 annual report, Secretary Ripley expressed the hope that, in cooperation with other institutions in Washington, an international center for advanced studies might be established. However, the Smithsonian is not a university; it grants no degrees and has no faculty or curriculum.

The Smithsonian is organized around its several bureaus and offices. Two organization charts are reproduced here, one showing the Smithsonian structure established in 1968 and

SMITHSONIAN INSTITUTION ORGANIZATION CHART

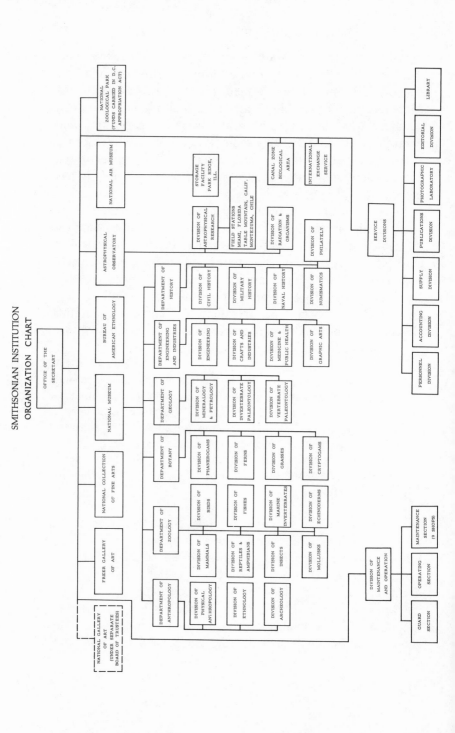

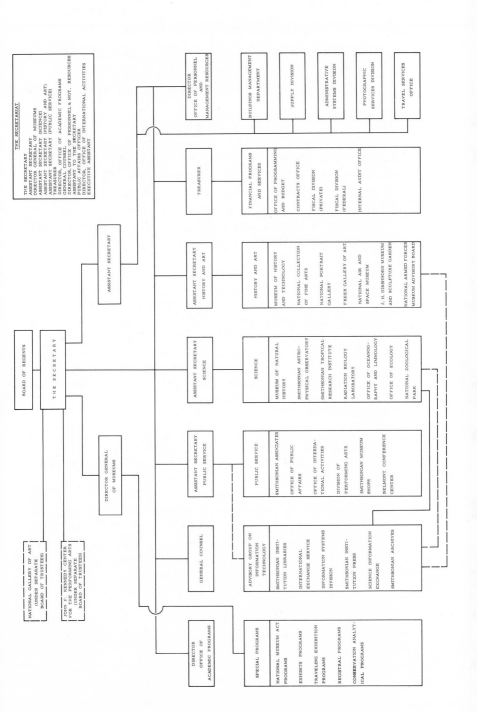

THE SECRETARIAT

THE SECRETARY
ASSISTANT SECRETARY
DIRECTOR GENERAL OF MUSEUMS
ASSISTANT SECRETARY (SCIENCE)
ASSISTANT SECRETARY (HISTORY AND ART)
ASSISTANT SECRETARY (PUBLIC SERVICE)
TREASURER
DIRECTOR, OFFICE OF ACADEMIC PROGRAMS
GENERAL COUNSEL
DIRECTOR, OFFICE OF PERSONNEL & MGT. RESOURCES
ASSISTANT TO THE SECRETARY
PUBLIC AFFAIRS OFFICER
DIRECTOR, OFFICE OF INTERNATIONAL ACTIVITIES
EXECUTIVE ASSISTANT

BOARD OF REGENTS

THE SECRETARY

NATIONAL GALLERY OF ART
(UNDER SEPARATE
BOARD OF TRUSTEES)

JOHN F. KENNEDY CENTER
FOR THE PERFORMING ARTS
(UNDER SEPARATE
BOARD OF TRUSTEES)

DIRECTOR GENERAL
OF MUSEUMS

GENERAL COUNSEL

DIRECTOR
OFFICE OF
ACADEMIC PROGRAMS

ASSISTANT SECRETARY

DIRECTOR
OFFICE OF PERSONNEL
AND
MANAGEMENT RESOURCES

BUILDINGS MANAGEMENT
DEPARTMENT

SUPPLY DIVISION

ADMINISTRATIVE
SYSTEMS DIVISION

PHOTOGRAPHIC
SERVICES DIVISION

TRAVEL SERVICES
OFFICE

TREASURER

FINANCIAL PROGRAMS
AND SERVICES

OFFICE OF PROGRAMMING
AND BUDGET

CONTRACTS OFFICE

FISCAL DIVISION
(PRIVATE)

FISCAL DIVISION
(FEDERAL)

INTERNAL AUDIT OFFICE

ASSISTANT SECRETARY
HISTORY AND ART

HISTORY AND ART

MUSEUM OF HISTORY
AND TECHNOLOGY

NATIONAL COLLECTION
OF FINE ARTS

NATIONAL PORTRAIT
GALLERY

FREER GALLERY OF ART

NATIONAL AIR AND
SPACE MUSEUM

J. H. HIRSHHORN MUSEUM
AND SCULPTURE GARDEN

NATIONAL ARMED FORCES
MUSEUM ADVISORY BOARD

ASSISTANT SECRETARY
SCIENCE

SCIENCE

MUSEUM OF NATURAL
HISTORY

SMITHSONIAN ASTRO-
PHYSICAL OBSERVATORY

SMITHSONIAN TROPICAL
RESEARCH INSTITUTE

RADIATION BIOLOGY
LABORATORY

OFFICE OF OCEANOG-
RAPHY AND LIMNOLOGY

OFFICE OF ECOLOGY

NATIONAL ZOOLOGICAL
PARK

ASSISTANT SECRETARY
PUBLIC SERVICE

PUBLIC SERVICE

SMITHSONIAN ASSOCIATES

OFFICE OF PUBLIC
AFFAIRS

OFFICE OF INTERNA-
TIONAL ACTIVITIES

DIVISION OF
PERFORMING ARTS

SMITHSONIAN MUSEUM
SHOPS

BELMONT CONFERENCE
CENTER

ADVISORY GROUP ON
INFORMATION
TECHNOLOGY

SMITHSONIAN INSTI-
TUTION LIBRARIES

INTERNATIONAL
EXCHANGE SERVICE

INFORMATION SYSTEMS
DIVISION

SMITHSONIAN INSTI-
TUTION PRESS

SCIENCE INFORMATION
EXCHANGE

SMITHSONIAN ARCHIVES

SPECIAL PROGRAMS

NATIONAL MUSEUM ACT
PROGRAMS

EXHIBITS PROGRAMS

TRAVELING EXHIBITION
PROGRAMS

REGISTRAL PROGRAMS

CONSERVATION ANALYT-
ICAL PROGRAMS

the other in 1948. Comparison of these charts demonstrates the degree of growth and complexity of the Institution.

The 1948 chart shows a relatively direct and uncomplicated arrangement, with lines of authority clearly indicated. The breakdown is according to organizational unit—bureau, department, division, section—in a more or less traditional fashion. The 1968 chart shows an over-all mushrooming— more assistant secretaries, more bureaus, more offices—and an attempt to reorganize, at least as far as the law allows, along program lines.

In a recent annual report Secretary Ripley discussed the rationale behind this new organization:

> The Smithsonian has endeavored to establish an organization that is adaptive to change and is experientially motivated— one with programs and structural modules predicated upon sociological interrelationships rather than upon compartmentalized bureaucratic boundaries, one in which individual as well as common goals can be achieved. . . . The Smithsonian is committed, in short, to a program of administration and management that recognizes the importance of individual fulfillment within the framework of its larger objectives.

This worthy objective would seem to make the preparation of an organization chart something of a nightmare.

In his book on the Smithsonian, Geoffrey T. Hellman characterized the Institution thus:

> Conceived by its first Secretary as primarily a scientific-research and scientific-research-disseminating body, it is today a unique congeries of thirteen governmental, or quasi-governmental, units in which science, art, the humanities, and a few things that seem to fall somewhere in between are conjoined in an impressive, if rather helter-skelter, manner.

It is true that the organization is not so close-knit as it was in earlier days. For many years, the Institution enjoyed more the atmosphere of a small college, where everyone knew everyone else, than that of a large university, where individuals are swallowed up as though by an octopus. The old-time *esprit de corps,* the unhurried way in which things were done with little fuss and a minimum of red tape, the old noncomplexity—all were indeed refreshing. Today, probably inevitably, the Smithsonian is suffering from bigness due to the expansion and increase of services to the public, to the exigencies of the geometric progression of modern science, sometimes to the ambitions of administrators perhaps too anxious to project a new image. Every bureau and office of the Institution has felt the change, but most staff members would agree that with the bigness have come a new vitality and a readiness to plunge into new programs and projects.

Evidence of a growing recognition within the Smithsonian administration of the need for cooperation with the outside world was the establishment in 1966 of a Smithsonian Council (not shown on the organization chart) whose status, it is hoped, will prove to be more active and less supernumerary than that of the Establishment. As planned, the council is to be a sort of grass-roots body of advisers, the "eyes and ears" of the Institution, so to speak. The council, consisting of not more than twenty-five members, meets regularly to advise on matters affecting the progress of science and learning within the Smithsonian and to "appraise opportunities for Smithsonian contributions to the advancement of public understanding and positive knowledge in those fields of science, learning, and the arts of primary interest to the Institution." Council members are appointed on the basis of "distinguished attainments in scholarship, research, and understanding" and are drawn principally from those active in the learned professions. The members, probably a little vague themselves about what their job is, are "invited to discuss the intellectual and cultural aspects of Institution activities with its officers and professional staff members." Just how this rather high-sounding plan for outside advice will translate into useful action remains to be seen. The council at the moment is too young a body in the life of the Institution to be judged, but the idea behind it does seem to promote the Henryesque notion that the Smithsonian should strive against parochialism and that the seeking of outside participation strengthens its position in the world of learning by providing a fringe source of fruitful ideas and constructive criticism.

Clearly, it is necessary that the multifarious activities on the Mall and beyond it be directed by men of strength within the organization itself and, to some degree, channeled from the outside by other men representing the scholarly disciplines in the sciences and the humanities. At present, the Institution's programs can be grouped roughly in four categories: museum functions, research activities, the arts, and service functions. But even these areas intermingle and overlap. Research is done at nearly all levels; museology is where you find it, and more and more Smithsonian activities, as the next four chapters show, tend to be interdisciplinary.

V

Museums as Repositories
and as Centers of Learning

From its founding, the Smithsonian Institution was directed to maintain a museum. At that time there were few museums in the United States, and the popular notion of a museum was not a temple of the Muses but a place to preserve objects, often of curious origin or nature. But there were men with grander ideas. George Brown Goode, in his classic paper "Museums of the Future," asserted that "no museum can grow and be respected which does not each year give additional proofs of its claims to be considered a center of learning." A century ago the United States was far behind the European nations in the development of museums; today it has caught up with, if not surpassed, them, not only quantitatively but qualitatively. But it took a long time to transform the old concept of a museum. It was 1889 when Goode wrote in his paper:

> The museum of the past must be set aside, reconstructed, transformed from a cemetery of bric-a-brac into a nursery of living thoughts. The museum of the future must stand side by side with the library and the laboratory, as a part of the teaching equipment of the college and university, and in the great cities cooperate with the public library as one of the principal agencies for the enlightenment of the people.

The essence of this philosophy has certainly guided the

Smithsonian museums since Goode's day and is apparent in their management and development today. Few could have been expected to foresee how Smithsonian museums were to grow in size, number, and stature as truly educational institutions.

THE U.S. NATIONAL MUSEUM

In the beginning, the "Smithsonian museum" was provided for exclusively from the Smithson fund, but this arrangement soon proved inadequate, and Henry early began to petition Congress for help. Not until 1858, however, did federal money become available (for exhibition cases), and only then could it be said that the U.S. National Museum was established.

In its earliest days, displayed in the Smithsonian Building, the collection must have resembled Goode's "cemetery of bric-a-brac," but it must be noted that it contained some rather illustrious material. The beginning nucleus was probably the private natural-history collections that young Spencer Baird brought with him in a single freight car when he came to the Institution in 1850.*

Another early source of material was the National Institute, which was a forerunner of the National Museum and to which, in fact, the government had entrusted James Smithson's own cabinet of minerals. The National Institute was a Washington organization chartered by Congress in 1818 under the name Columbian Institute for the Promotion of Arts and Sciences. Its charter expired in 1838, but it arose from its ashes in 1840 and started life anew. Both it and the Smithsonian operated side by side until 1861, when the Institute was dissolved and its collections were turned over to the Smithsonian.

* The National Museum has had only eight directors: Spencer Fullerton Baird (1850–78), George Brown Goode (1878–96), Charles D. Walcott (1896–98), Richard Rathbun (1898–1918), William de C. Ravenel (1918–25), Alexander Wetmore (1925–48), A. Remington Kellogg (1948–62), and Frank A. Taylor (1962–   ).

A third source of materials was the Patent Office. The law incorporating the Smithsonian contained a provision that gave the Institution definite museum functions:

> All objects of art and of foreign and curious research, and all objects of natural history, plants, and geological and mineralogical specimens belonging to or hereafter to belong to the United States, which may be in the city of Washington, in whosesoever custody the same may be, shall be delivered to such persons as may be authorized by the Board of Regents to receive them.

This provision covered the so-called national cabinet of curiosities, then housed in the Patent Office Building, but the collection was not removed to the Smithsonian Building until 1857, by which time it had been definitely settled that Congress would make the necessary appropriations for the National Museum's maintenance.

Government exploring expeditions comprised still another source of museum material. Notable were the vast collections made by the U.S. Exploring Expedition led by Charles Wilkes —its material was among the "curiosities" that came from the National Institute in 1857—and the collections received from the several surveys organized by the War Department to explore a railroad route to the Pacific coast.

These were only the beginning. The phenomenal increase in the national collections can be followed year by year through the Institution's annual reports. Today, the total number of specimens in all departments is well over 64.5 million— about 80 per cent in natural history, the remainder in the arts, technology, and history. The largest aggregates numerically are in the fields of invertebrate zoology, paleontology, and philately.

The Smithsonian still depends a great deal on its own expeditions to bring in new materials to its museums, and it occasionally purchases objects directly. In addition, thousands of gifts come in every year from individuals and organizations. Though the Smithsonian makes good use of most private gifts, it need not and does not accept every one offered. The real desiderata always take precedence over the less desirable or less needed.*

There are, of course, two basic uses for museum collections —research and study, and educational exhibits—and, in both of these functions, the National Museum has long and conscientiously fulfilled its obligations. In the study of all branches of natural history, including man's material culture, the museum collections have become indispensable and fundamental to our knowledge of the world. Dr. Remington Kellogg, a former director of the museum, emphasized the importance of natural-history collections in *Science* magazine of August 9, 1946:

> The descriptive zoologist or botanist is concerned primarily with establishing diagnostic characters that differentiate living forms. By assembling for minute comparative study large series of specimens, all uniformly prepared or preserved, from all possible localities, taxonomists have been enabled constantly to advance human knowledge.

The National Museum's incomparable collections have been so used, intensively and increasingly, for over a century by scholars from all parts of the world.

Until 1957, the National Museum operated administratively as a single unit. When it became clear that the long-awaited dream of a new building to house the collections and exhibits

---

* Occasionally, a gift will have an aura of the bizarre and curious. A few years ago, for example, a well-known New England research establishment decided to disprove the ancient adage that a silk purse could not be made from a sow's ear. They did it, and though the finished product was undoubtedly chemically ingenious, it was neither silk nor a purse the likes of which had been seen before. But the simulation was impressive and unique, and, with suitable ceremony and press coverage, the purse was presented to the Smithsonian. Just which curator now "curates" it is unknown to me.

in science and technology was to become reality, the U.S. National Museum, the statutory entity, was divided into two units—the Museum of Natural History and the Museum of History and Technology, each operating under a director. In 1969, the names National Museum of Natural History and National Museum of History and Technology were adopted.

Although the office of over-all director of the National Museum was retained, it gradually became a figurehead position, and in the 1968 organization chart the term U.S. National Museum does not appear. In 1968, the director of the National Museum, Frank A. Taylor, was given the title director general of Museums. Taylor has explained that although there is no intent to abolish its name, at present it is more correct to describe the U.S. National Museum as a program and not as a museum with collections and projects in competition with other museums. Its primary activities will be research, experimentation, and modernization and expansion of museum functions, such as planning exhibits employing new technologies, introducing machine cataloguing of collections and referral systems, extending museum resources through circulation of exhibits or decentralizing collections, exploring methods of using reference collections in remote storage, issuing publications on museum techniques, extending consultation service to museums, cooperating with museum associations and regional conferences to provide standards of performance and accreditation, and encouraging more public support of American museums from federal and state governments. This program in large part is being contemplated under the National Museum Act of 1966.

In recent years, as the new Smithsonian buildings have provided more space for new and modernized exhibits, the national museums have been able to utilize their great reservoir of collections, together with the new material constantly coming in, to particularly good advantage. The Museum of Natural History currently draws about 3.5 million visitors annually; the Museum of History and Technology, nearly 6 million; and the National Air and Space Museum, about 2 million. This tremendous attendance cannot help but keep these museums on their toes, and it attests to the eminent success they have achieved in realizing the educational potential of their exhibits, which, in hall after hall, highlight the men, events, and material culture that are the warp and woof of our national history, reincarnating those vestiges of time that inspire in young and old the sense of wonder that lies at the roots of knowledge.*

THE NATIONAL MUSEUM OF NATURAL HISTORY

The job of a museum of natural history is to preserve and portray the record of the living world, of man and his environment, both past and present. It builds up a storehouse of knowledge of the earth's peoples, animals, plants, fossils, and minerals and attempts to present this knowledge to visitors in a scientifically accurate, meaningful, graphic, and attractive manner. Three interdependent elements are basic—the collections, the exhibits, and the staff members who study and organize the material.

To the visitor, the most obviously impressive sights at the National Museum of Natural History are the permanent exhibit halls, which in recent years have benefited by the Smithsonian's program of exhibit modernization. To describe all of them here, colorful and exciting as they are, would take undue space, but a few of the most outstanding should be mentioned. The Hall of Life in the Sea, a favorite of visitors, contains a great model of a gigantic blue whale, a tour de force

* In Langley's time, and for many years thereafter, there was a hall directly across from the main entrance in the Smithsonian Building called the Children's Room, over whose portal was the inscription "Knowledge Begins in Wonder." Full of exhibits geared to the interests and understanding of the child, the room was Langley's creation and his special ward. It was long a special attraction.

of taxidermy that takes one's breath away. The magnificent Hall of Gems and Minerals features the Hope Diamond, the equally famous Napoleon necklace, and other priceless specimens. The Hall of Fossil Plants and Invertebrates portrays the scientific record of the early development of life on this planet. The Hall of Fossil Fishes, Amphibians, and Reptiles displays selections from the museum's superb collections of these creatures, which represent the most primitive groups of backboned animals. The Hall of the Age of Mammals in North America re-creates a mammalian world that existed before modern man appeared. The Hall of Latin American Archeology illustrates the wide range of early cultures in Latin America, from the simple hunting-and-fishing people to the civilizations of the Incas, Mayas, and Aztecs. The Hall of North American Archeology deals with the prehistoric cultures of the Eskimo and the American Indians of the Far North, the North Pacific Coast, California, and the Southwest. The American Indian Hall deals with the Eskimo and the Indians of the Eastern Woodlands, the Great Plains, and the North Pacific Coast, featuring particularly their arts and customs. Other permanent exhibit halls include the Hall of the World of Mammals, the Hall of North American Mammals, and the Hall of the Birds of the World. There are also special exhibits, such as the Fénykövi elephant, the largest specimen of the African bush elephant on record, which stands in the great rotunda facing the visitor as he enters the building from the south.

If the visitor is fortunate, he may get a glimpse behind the scenes at the museum and come away equally impressed by the endless cabinets filled with what the curators call the study collections of the museum. They contain millions of specimens of insects, mollusks, birds, mammals, fishes, plants, fossils, minerals, and anthropological artifacts, all classified and catalogued, constituting a permanent scientific documentation of what we know of our earth and its inhabitants.

The National Museum of Natural History is today organized

under seven departments: anthropology, including the divisions of Latin American anthropology, Old World anthropology, North American anthropology, and physical anthropology; botany, with divisions of phanerogams, ferns, grasses, cryptogams, plant anatomy, and fungi; entomology, including the divisions of neuropteroids, Lepidoptera and Diptera, Coleoptera, Hemiptera and Hymenoptera, and Myriapoda and Arachnida; invertebrate zoology, with divisions of Crustacea, echinoderms, worms, and mollusks; mineral sciences, with divisions of meteorites, mineralogy, and petrology; paleobiology, including divisions of invertebrate paleontology, vertebrate paleontology, palebotany, and sedimentology; and vertebrate zoology, with divisions of fishes, reptiles and amphibians, birds, and mammals. Each department is headed by a chairman and each division by a supervisor-curator.

A curator's job is essentially to take care of the collections. His work includes cataloguing, identifying, and classifying acquisitions in his division, conducting research on the division collections, overseeing publication of research results, playing host to outside investigators, and keeping abreast of the literature in his area. He must keep himself thoroughly familiar with all that is under his care. Furthermore, he is expected to plan, oversee construction, and maintain exhibits for the general public. He also participates in the Institution's program of exploration and field work, attends meetings, and makes speeches. His is not a part-time job. It requires hard work, a breadth of knowledge, a certain degree of administrative ability, and a knack for getting along with people.

These diverse requirements, almost impossible to find adequately in one person, make the curator's lot not always a happy one and are beginning to shake museum administrators. Indeed, in the March, 1969, issue of *Museum News*, Dr. Donald F. Squires, a deputy director of the Museum of Natural History who left the Smithsonian to direct marine research at another institution, expressed his belief that this multiplicity of abilities and conflicting activities required of museum curators, particularly in natural-history museums, is forcing the "curatorial staff to adopt a corresponding 'multiple' view toward their careers" and is causing a certain "schizophrenia of these museums." He thinks that the museum, faced with the need to employ a diversity of types of persons to carry out these roles, "lacks a philosophy, a rationale, a criterion for employment."

The curators at the Smithsonian are also becoming more and more involved in its increasing international, academic, extension, seminar, public-affairs, and other programs that cut across department and divisional lines. All agree that these activities are contributing to the museums' attainment of Goode's ideal of a true "center of learning," but they complain that there are only twenty-four hours in a day. Relief does not appear in sight.

Within the National Museum, the Department of Botany administers the U.S. National Herbarium, a quasi-official name for an organization whose origins date from the founding of the Smithsonian. It was established in 1894 as the name for the joint plant collections of the Smithsonian and the U.S. Department of Agriculture. The herbarium has had a long and distinguished history and deserves a fuller account than space here will allow. For many years housed in commodious quarters on the third floor and in the towers of the Smithsonian Building, the herbarium was moved to the new west wing of the Museum of Natural History in 1965. Its collections of plants now comprise one of the largest of their kind in the world, numbering well over 3 million specimens preserved in more than two thousand storage cases. They are the basis for world-wide botanical studies of scientific and economic importance. The Smithsonian has published about forty volumes in the series Contributions from the United States National Herbarium.

THE NATIONAL MUSEUM OF HISTORY AND TECHNOLOGY

The task of the National Museum of History and Technology is to preserve and portray records illustrating the history of science and engineering and the cultural development of the United States since the discovery of America. Though the building housing its activities is new, many of its collections date from the early days of the Institution. As a recent guidebook stated, the museum "is a product of the Smithsonian's century and more of experience in developing museums for the enlightenment of scholars and the instruction and pleasure of visitors. It places before the millions who visit the nation's capital each year a stimulating exposition that commemorates our heritage of freedom and illustrates our way of life." It is a monument to American ingenuity, industry, enterprise, creativity, and material progress.

Here, as with the Museum of Natural History, the creation of new exhibits and the task of keeping them current must go hand in hand with the development of the study collections and the research carried out upon them.

When the museum first occupied its new building in January, 1964, ten exhibition halls were ready for visitors. Since then, several more of the approximately fifty permanent exhibit halls planned have been completed. In all, they comprise a prodigious and dazzling display. One of the most impressive features is the manner in which many of the nation's unique treasures—the original "Star-Spangled Banner," Thomas Jefferson's writing desk, Samuel Morse's telegraph, Benjamin Franklin's printing press, Eli Whitney's model of his cotton gin, the *John Bull* locomotive, and Joseph Henry's electromagnet—are integrated into the thematic treatment of the halls yet at the same time given due special prominence.

One of the museum's most ambitious exhibit projects has

been designated Growth of the United States. Two of the five halls planned are completed, each representing a century of American life. Hall II covers the period 1640 to 1750 and Hall III, 1750 to 1851. When the remaining halls are opened, the total display will serve as a kind of index to the museum for, by its nature, the exhibit transects the museum's divisional lines. Objects from the arts, technology, and science from each century of American experience will be interpreted in the context of the individual periods.

The Hall of Everyday Life in the American Past is equally outstanding. Individual components include exhibits on European backgrounds; New England furnishings of the early eighteenth century; a complete log house originally built about 1740 in Mill Creek Hundred, Delaware; a lavishly paneled parlor from a 4-room plantation house of Isle of Wight County, Virginia; a kitchen from a frontier ranch house built about 1860 in California; a complete confectionery shop of 1900 from Georgetown, D.C.; and displays of American folk pottery and lighting devices.

Another colorful hall depicts four centuries of costume in America; another demonstrates the growth of American politics and the contributions of various individuals, groups, and institutions in the nation's history. The exhibit of the gowns of the First Ladies of the White House, arranged in authentic period settings, is justly celebrated. It forms a panorama of formal feminine attire from the time of Martha Washington to the present.

In addition to the permanent halls, there are permanent exhibits based on such themes as the Armed Forces of the United States; orders, medals, and decorations; underwater exploration; the graphic arts; photography; monetary history and medallic art; philately and postal history; musical instruments; ceramics; glass; a Foucault pendulum; farm machinery; road vehicles; American merchant shipping; railroads; bridges and tunnels; heavy machinery; electricity; tools; timekeepers, record players, typewriters, and locks; physical sciences; medical sciences; manufactures; textiles; petroleum; coal, iron and steel; and nuclear energy. Galleries on the first and third floors are frequently used for temporary displays of newly acquired collections, traveling exhibitions, or private collections on loan. Indeed, it would take several days to view adequately all the exhibits in the Museum of History and Technology. There are too many to be described here in detail, but among their great wealth and variety is something of special interest for everyone.

The over-all activities of the museum are organized into five departments, each of which has a chairman and a supervisor-curator: applied arts, including divisions of graphic arts and photography, numismatics, postal history, and textiles; cultural history, with divisions of costume and furnishings, ethnic and Western cultural history, music history, and pre-industrial history; industries, with divisions of agriculture and mining, ceramics and glass, manufacturing, and transportation; national and military history, including divisions of historic archeology, military history, naval history, and political history; and science and technology, with divisions of electricity and nuclear energy, mechanical and civil engineering, medical sciences, and physical sciences.

The National Air and Space Museum

The Smithsonian's interest in aeronautics is of long standing. It has been a persistent interest, founded upon the foresight of those who saw in man's dream for wings something more than wishful thinking and whose faith in man's ability to fly was founded on an understanding of the physics of flight. As early as 1861, Joseph Henry assisted and encouraged the pioneer aeronaut Thaddeus S. C. Lowe in his balloon experiments and helped him gain an audience with President Abraham Lincoln, which led to the use of balloons in the Civil War. The Smithsonian annual report for 1863 carried an article entitled "Aeronautic Voyages Performed with a View to the Advancement of Science" by James Smithson's friend Arago and an account of the balloon ascensions of the British aeronaut James Glaisher. In article after article in the reports of succeeding years, the history of human flight can be traced.

The tradition of aeronautics at the Institution was given a tremendous boost, of course, by Secretary Langley, who not only pioneered in the science and practice of flying but also possessed a great interest in museum collections, which resulted, as Paul E. Garber wrote in his handbook *The National Aeronautical Collections,* "in the acquisition of valuable aircraft material of the pioneer era [including Langley's own flying machines] and the wonderful aeronautical library he assembled," which is now in the Smithsonian's possession.

The national aeronautical collections were actually started with a group of kites obtained from the Chinese Imperial Commission at the close of the Philadelphia Centennial in 1876. From this acorn grew the great oak that today constitutes the largest and best collection of historic aeronautical material in the world.

In 1932 these collections, which grew constantly in quantity and quality as the Age of Flight progressed, were put under the jurisdiction of the aeronautics section in the National Museum's Department of Engineering and Industries and were housed in the Arts and Industries Building. Space for the exhibition of full-sized airplanes and other items was a problem. After World War I, a sizable hangarlike building that had been used for testing wartime installations of the Liberty engine became available. Situated on the Smithsonian grounds, it first accommodated several military planes of the time and has since become the principal showroom of the collection. It is usually known as the Aircraft Building.

With the continuing increment of important material and

with the growing recognition of the importance of the collection for aeronautical education, agitation grew to make the museum a separate entity. By Act of Congress, signed by President Harry S. Truman on August 12, 1946, the National Air Museum, renamed the National Air and Space Museum in 1966, was established as a separate Smithsonian bureau. It is administered with the assistance of an advisory board, of which the Secretary of the Smithsonian is a member. The Act directed that the new museum "shall memorialize the national development of aviation; collect, preserve, and display aeronautical equipment of historical interest and significance; serve as a repository for scientific equipment and data pertaining to the development of aviation; and provide educational material for the historical study of aviation." More than thirty-five hundred items that had accumulated during the previous seventy-one years formed the nucleus of the new agency's collections.

Exhibit space is still a problem that will have to be resolved before the National Air and Space Museum will come into its own. Although a goodly number of full-sized planes and space craft have been on exhibition—the Langley models and aerodromes, the Wright brothers' *Kitty Hawk Flyer,* Charles Lindbergh's *Spirit of St. Louis,* Wiley Post's *Winnie Mae,* the B-29 atomic bomber *Enola Gay,* the supersonic Bell X-1, and the space capsules of John Glenn and Alan Shepard—many more have had to be preserved in storage facilities outside Washington. However, progress has been made toward the realization of a new building for the National Air and Space Museum. A site has been selected on the Mall a few blocks east of the present Smithsonian campus, and architectural plans and models have been approved. On July 19, 1966, exactly twenty years after the museum was formally established, President Johnson signed the bill authorizing the erection of the new building, but Congress has yet to appropriate funds for construction.

A recent development of the museum is the signing of a joint agreement between the Smithsonian and the National Aeronautics and Space Administration whereby all historically important air and space artifacts developed by NASA will be transferred to the museum after their technical evaluation is completed. The museum has also set up a historical research center whose primary objective is to collect, compile, and make available to researchers and historians data relating to aerospace science and technology.

A NATIONAL ARMED FORCES MUSEUM

It is not strictly correct, as yet, to refer to a National Armed Forces Museum, inasmuch as it exists only in the form of an advisory board within the Smithsonian organization, with an executive director and staff planning for the future. But it is a museum in the making and some day will undoubtedly burst into bloom. The project began in January, 1958, when President Dwight D. Eisenhower appointed a committee of distinguished private citizens and public servants to look into the possibility of establishing a U.S. armed forces museum comparable to similar institutions in Europe in the belief that such a museum could "make substantial contributions to our citizens' knowledge and understanding of American life." Under the aegis of the committee, headed by Chief Justice Earl Warren, a study was made of European military museums and was submitted to the President. Then in August, 1961, P.L. 87-186 established the National Armed Forces Museum Advisory Board to assist and advise the Smithsonian Board of Regents on matters concerning the portrayal of the contributions that the U.S. Armed Forces have made to American society and culture, the investigation of lands and buildings in and near the District of Columbia suitable for the museum, and the preparation of a recommendation to Congress with respect to the acquisition of such lands and buildings. Inherent in this, of course, was the intention that such a museum would in fact be established under the Smithsonian, and the law specified that the Institution begin preparing for a U.S. military museum that shall

1. commemorate and display the contributions made by the military forces of the Nation toward creating, developing, and maintaining a free, peaceful, and independent society and culture in this country

2. portray the valor and sacrificial service of the men and women in the Armed Forces as an inspiration to the present and future generations of America

3. demonstrate the demands placed upon the energies of our people, the hardships endured, and the sacrifice demanded in our constant search for world peace

4. graphically describe the extensive peacetime contribution the Armed Forces have made to the advance of human knowledge in science, nuclear energy, polar and space exploration, electronics, engineering, aeronautics, and medicine

5. interpret through dramatic display significant current problems affecting the Nation's security

6. provide a study center for scholarly research into the meaning of war, its effects on civilization, and the role of the Armed Forces in maintaining a just and lasting peace by providing a powerful deterrent to war.

Acting on this mandate from Congress, the advisory board and its staff have set about making the museum a reality. Federal funds totaling $125,000 were made available for the museum in the 1967 fiscal year. Potential sites in the Washington area were considered for the proposed National Armed Forces Historical Museum Park and a projected study center to be designated the Dwight D. Eisenhower Center for Historical Research. In his 1967 annual report, the director of the advisory board, Col. John H. Macgruder, 3d, stated that a site in the Fort Foote area of Prince Georges County, Maryland, had been approved by the Board of Regents and the National Capital Planning Commission, and progress had been made toward acquiring it. As this is written, congressional approval has not yet been given.

The whole scheme has been opposed by a few individuals and groups who see such a museum as a potential glorification of war and who are not convinced of the wisdom of establishing an organization that might seem to memorialize what they consider evil. Others, equally peace-loving, hold that the nation's military history, for better or worse, ought to be preserved and studied and that to ignore the impact that military security plays in modern civilization is to bury one's head in the sand. Certainly it was the philosophy of the lawmakers who authorized the creation of the museum that it is in the best interests of all, even those who violently oppose war on religious or philosophic grounds, to understand the role of the armed forces in our society and to encourage educational facilities intended to promote such understanding. Colonel Macgruder, in answer to the criticisms aimed at the museum, stated in a letter that "every effort is being made to alleviate any possible accusation that the Smithsonian is a propaganda agency of the Department of Defense or a special pleader for current policies."

The advisory board, under the chairmanship of Smithsonian Regent John Nicholas Brown, is proceeding, as opportunity offers, to acquire objects that eventually will find their place in the museum, particularly material that, if not acquired immediately, would not be available in the future, such as specimens of obsolete matériel, prototypes, and similar items that normally would be disposed of by the Department of Defense or other holding agencies. Among the items already acquired is the bathyscaphe *Trieste I*. This vessel pioneered in underwater exploration and holds the record for deep dives, having reached the bottom of Challenger Deep, some seven miles below the water's surface off the Marianas in the western Pacific Ocean.

A recent project that has attracted considerable popular attention is the salvaging of the Union monitor *Tecumseh* from the bottom of Mobile Bay, where it has rested since the battle there on August 5, 1864. In spite of Admiral Farragut's immortal utterance, "Damn the torpedoes! Full speed ahead!" the *Tecumseh* went down in less than a minute with most of her crew. Supported by private funds of nearly $5 million, the salvaging operations are expected to bring up the vessel intact from the sand and silt in which it has been protectively encased for more than a hundred years. It will form a fine exhibit, a capsulized glimpse of the U.S. Navy of the Civil War period.

The National Zoological Park

The National Zoological Park came into being shortly after Langley became Smithsonian Secretary in 1887 and developed under his personal guidance. "Langley," wrote Cyrus Adler in his autobiography *I Have Remembered the Days,* "had an eager curiosity about animal life and a great love for natural scenes, and so it fell to him, the astronomer, to move successfully in establishing the Park." The zoo collection actually began under Secretary Baird, when there was created in the National Museum a Department of Living Animals to take care of gifts that began coming in to the government from generous citizens. Three American elk, for example, were donated by Buffalo Bill Cody. By 1888, the department had about 225 animals to care for, many of which were housed in a paddock on the south side of the Smithsonian Building. This arrangement must have delighted the inhabitants of southwest Washington when the wind was from the north. The "curator" of this menagerie was William T. Hornaday, a taxidermist and ardent explorer who later became an effective conservationist, head of the New York Zoological Park, and a distinguished and voluminous writer on natural history.

It was at this time that the American bison was making its last stand. Only a few scattered herds remained, and Hornaday attempted to arouse public interest in preserving them. The fate of the buffalo, he thought, should be a sad object lesson, and, in the National Museum annual report for 1886–87, there appeared his work *The Extermination of the American Bison,* a valuable natural-history document that focused public attention on the need for conserving American big-game species. Hornaday's "zoo" contained six captive buffaloes, and both he and Langley believed that if this "herd" could be increased and exhibited in Washington, the educational work of conservation would be greatly furthered.

Langley and Hornaday had already made a survey of possible sites for such a "zoological garden" in the capital and agreed that the valley of Rock Creek, with its woods and waters, rocky cliffs, picturesque hillsides, and other attractive features, would make an ideal location and would be well adapted for wild animals. For several years, the Smithsonian had been using its own slim funds to feed and house the animals in temporary and overcrowded quarters. But sentiment for a national zoo was building, in Congress and throughout the country, and finally, in 1889, Congress passed a bill for the establishment of a National Zoological Park in the District of Columbia for the "advancement of science and the instruction and recreation of the people."

Langley had fought patiently and hard in support of the zoo. In an article in *Century Magazine* in 1900, the naturalist Ernest Thompson Seton described Langley's efforts to get the bill through Congress:

Altogether the Secretary of the Smithsonian found it no easy bill to carry, though it was endorsed by nearly every scientist and educator in the country. . . . Fierce battles had to be fought with ignorant and captious politicans. One objected that he did not see why the people should pay "to have the Nebraska elk and Florida alligators cooped up." If they had to spend money for it they would want things they could not see at home—dog-faced baboons, kangaroos, man-eating tigers, etc. Another, a fervent patriot, objected to any money being spent on exotic species, as it was contrary to the spirit of the Constitution to encourage or import foreigners! . . . After three years of persistent effort, involving vastly more worry than the management of the whole Smithsonian for three times that period, Mr. Langley succeeded in carrying both Houses of Congress over the successive stages of ridicule, toleration, and favorable consideration, to the point of accepting and providing for the scheme.

The year after the zoo was established, it was placed under the direction of the Smithsonian Institution; an appropriation of $200,000 was made for the purchase of land, and a commission was appointed to select and obtain the site. Hornaday became the first superintendent, but he resigned at the end of a year over differences of opinion about the plans for the Park.

Langley wisely began drawing up a comprehensive plan for the new enterprise to provide for orderly growth for the future. Frederick Law Olmsted, the eminent landscape architect who designed more than eighty public parks including New York's Central Park and Philadelphia's Fairmount Park, was commissioned to lay out the zoo park, which today occupies about 150 acres of land. The grounds were cleared and improved, the required roads were constructed, one animal house was built, and the zoo was in business. Former Smithsonian editor W. P. True has recorded that "in a borrowed wagon, all the animals that had been kept in the sheds of the Smithsonian—some 185 strong—made the journey to their new home, and the National Zoological Park was opened to the public."

Growth of the zoo was to be expected, and by 1895 it had become so flourishing that it could lend thirteen animals to a circus. By 1910, the daily average of visitors was about

1,400. By 1926, the number of animals had grown to 1,700. Today, the number of animals totals about 3,300, and the number of visitors is estimated at about 5 million annually. It has become one of the largest and best zoos in the country. Director Theodore H. Reed stated in 1967 that the zoo then contained not only more individual animals but also a greater number of species than ever before in its history. Accessions come from several sources: gifts from individuals, organizations, and governments; purchases; exchanges with other zoos and circuses; births; and special collecting expeditions. Important among the last-named have been the Smithsonian-Chrysler Expedition to Tanganyika, East Africa, in 1926; the National Geographic-Smithsonian Expedition to the East Indies in 1937; and the Smithsonian-Firestone Expedition to Liberia in 1940—all of which resulted in the addition of many hundred rare and interesting animals for the collection.

One of the zoo's proud possessions today is Mohini, a rare Indian white tiger of Rewa and a great favorite with visitors. Among Mohini's half a dozen or so offspring have been two white cubs; the surviving one, Rewata, is also a great favorite at the zoo.

In recent years, through a reorganization of its work and a reassessment of its functions and potential, the zoo has been able to place more emphasis on research. A scientific research department was established in 1965, headed by a resident scientist. New facilities include housing for animals under study and rooms where tropical and cold climates can be maintained, all removed from public exhibition areas and designed to encourage flexible research. The zoo's veterinary division, whose staff now includes a pathologist, also participates in the research program.

In 1961, the zoo began a 12-year program of physical redevelopment to encompass the entire park complex. Funds for this are being provided piecemeal through appropriations from Congress, which at long last realized that if the National

Zoological Park were to fulfill its educational obligations to the millions of visitors to the capital, as well as to the local residents, it must begin to renovate and rehabilitate a plant that after nearly ninety years had begun to look a little seedy. In the first phase of the program, the birdhouse was extensively remodeled and a large outdoor flight cage was built. New facilities for hoofed animals were completed in 1966. The next phase called for a new animal hospital, which is now under way. Unfortunately, because of the lag in federal appropriations, the program is three years behind schedule.

Today the zoo is placing renewed emphasis on conservation of endangered species in harmony with Langley's conception that the National Zoological Park was to be "a home and city of refuge for the vanishing races of the continent." The zoo is becoming a center for the collection and distribution of vanishing animals, not only of this continent but also of the rest of the world, and is participating in agreements to restrict traffic in illegally procured animals and to promote inter-zoo breeding arrangements. A conservation farm for propagation and research is a gleam in the eye of the present director.

MUSEUM EXHIBIT PROGRAMS

Museum exhibit programs must dovetail with research activities. The work of opening up new halls and keeping the exhibitions up to date as new materials come in and new techniques become available goes on year after year. In these operations, the curators work closely with the Institution's over-all Office of Exhibits, whose staff includes some of the best and most experienced museum technicians and designers in the country. Together, they plan and execute not only the exhibits for the permanent halls but also the many short-term and often short-notice displays, which continually enliven the museums with fresh and topical materials.

Many visitors are particularly impressed with the unique quality of the objects on display. There is only one Hope Diamond, one Fénykövi elephant, one *Spirit of St. Louis,* and it is before them. The exhibits are modern in technique and in many instances are the first of their kind in the world. More and more their direct emphasis and underlying philosophy are geared to education for the public, and the public appears to be delighted with this approach.

The magnitude and variety of the exhibits are illustrated by one year's output. The Office of Exhibits reported that in 1968 the exhibits staff assigned to the Museum of History and Technology produced forty-seven special exhibits and worked on eight permanent exhibits. During the same period, the Museum of Natural History exhibits laboratory produced seven special exhibits and made progress on six permanent halls, and the National Air and Space Museum arranged ten special exhibits. The subjects of the exhibits were, among others, Peruvian silver, Mexican prints, computers, political cartoons, Appalachian poverty, organ-making, the art of organic forms, flora and fauna of the Chesapeake Bay, and early religious art of Mexico. A few of the permanent halls advanced during 1968 were those featuring autos and coaches, textiles, electricity, musical instruments, nuclear energy, Pacific-Asian ethnology, African-Asian ethnology, gems, and the Lockheed "Vega" aircraft used by Amelia Earhart.

The Smithsonian's recent move toward centralization of functions and services is evident in the exhibits program. Frank A. Taylor, director general of Museums, elaborated upon the trend in a letter:

> Starting years ago with such matters as security, maintenance, and operations of buildings, today museum education, academic programs, sales shops, associates programs, public affairs, performing arts, and many other activities that normally go on in museums are managed centrally. . . . Exhibits design and production have become increasingly centralized, serving

additional museums. Exhibits of certain types now originate without curatorial participation, and a study is being made that will consider whether the public exhibition areas in all Smithsonian buildings should not be considered as an opportunity to engage in more social action and broader relevant interdisciplinary movements than usually concern the individual curators. The thought is that the exhibits function would be centralized with its own staff of scientists and historians who would have no authority or responsibility over space or subject matter as such.

If adopted, this arrangement would indeed modify traditional curatorial functions.

More and more museums are denying George Santayana's thought, expressed more than half a century ago, that "an artist may visit a museum, but only a pedant can live there." My young granddaughter once exclaimed as she was being taken through one of the Smithsonian's buildings, "Gee, I would like to live here!" Behind the exhibitions' construction and documentation lies no end of scholarship, but the pedantry has disappeared. To the millions who view the exhibits every year, they appeal, of course, in many ways. As in music and painting and poetry, their beauty lies in their diversity and power to inspire the visitor according to his individual needs. Once I escorted Franklin P. Adams through some of the Smithsonian halls. The next day, February 13, 1936, he wrote in his column in the *New York Herald Tribune:*

Out, into the iciest, slipperiest morning ever I . . . went to see P. Oehser at the Smithsonian Institution, and mighty much interested in some of it, but not the natural history portion. But I will be bound that there are thousands of Americans who have visited the museums and galleries of France and Italy who would scorn to go to the Smithsonian, yet were the same thing in these foreign lands they would not dare to come home and say they had not seen it, yet would be the first to scream about the Constitution, and down with the traitor and up with the star.

Adams was especially impressed with the printing press used by Benjamin Franklin as a journeyman printer in London in 1726. "That," he wrote, "was seeing Shelley plain, and I defy anybody who ever has passed through a composing room once not to remove his hat when gazing on that sacred relic."

VI

Smithsonian Research

Research in the sciences, technologies, and arts is so inseparable a part of Smithsonian concern that to devote a separate chapter to it is to highlight much that is contained in other portions of this book. Research is the backbone of the Smithsonian, and it goes out to the world through the Institution's exhibits, publications, lectures, and nearly every other activity.

Smithsonian research began, of course, with James Smithson's prescription for the increase of knowledge. Joseph Henry, in his original program enjoined the Institution to "enlarge the existing stock of knowledge by the addition of new truths," and, as a research scientist himself, he firmly set the pattern for the future. At first Henry's role was principally that of an organizer of science, for the Smithsonian had few research men on its staff for many years. It could and did, however, provide a focal point for research, encouraging the work of outside scientists and, in some instances, even furnishing them living quarters in the Smithsonian Building, aiding in the publication of their works, and in other ways supporting the scientific endeavor of Smithsonian cooperators. As the years passed and as the museum collections accumulated to the point where they could serve as the foundation of research, the Smithsonian's own research expanded intramurally.

In his 1895 essay on "The Principles of Museum Administration" George Brown Goode defined a museum's obligation to research. Its duty, he wrote, is "to aid learned men in the work of extending the boundaries of knowledge, by affording them the use of material for investigation, laboratories, and appliances" and "to stimulate original research in connection with its own collections, and to promote the publications of the results." It would be difficult to find an apter description of the aims of museum research. The Smithsonian has hewed to this line, and in every branch of the Institution today, whether it be anthropology, biology, aeronautics, ecology, history, the arts, astrophysics, or the technologies, research is a consuming activity. Every annual report describes in considerable detail the projects carried out by the staff. Three examples illustrate the types and variety of research that goes on year after year in nearly every division, at home and abroad. Other research activities are referred to elsewhere as various Smithsonian bureaus are described.

1965   S. K. Hamarneh spent the period June 29 through October 17, 1964, in a research tour of ten Middle Eastern countries and Spain. In addition to assembling manuscript data for a history of medicine in medieval Islam, he collected data for indexing the medical manuscripts in the Zahiriyak National Library, Damascus.

1967   The monographic study of the crustose coralline algae of the North Atlantic took Walter H. Adey to the coasts of Ireland and Norway, where he made extensive collections of living corallines for anatomical study and, at the same time, he conducted ecological studies of these poorly known organisms. By the end of the year he had extended his shipboard research program as far south along the European coast as Great Britain.

1968   J. Lawrence Angel extended his field-work in Turkey on the health, energy, fertility, and genetic patterns of the earliest farming peoples. He confirmed that their smaller body size and poorer dental health in contrast to those of the meat-eating successful hunters of latest Paleolithic times, was a consequence of chronic falciparum malaria (indicated by anemia-produced thickening of the skull vault) and their carbohydrate diet. Yet the farmers' greater certainty of food supply allowed a slight increase in longevity and in fecundity.

THE BUREAU OF AMERICAN ETHNOLOGY (1879–1964)

The Bureau of American Ethnology (BAE) or "the Bureau," as it has been called (as if it were the only bureau in the Smithsonian) no longer exists as such, but it has played so important a role in the Institution's history that it deserves a sort of *Requiescat in pace* recognition. Technically, it passed into history as a separate organization on July 29, 1964, when it was merged with the National Museum's Department of Anthropology to form the Smithsonian Office of Anthropology, but its memory lingers on.

Founded in 1879 with John Wesley Powell as the first director, the bureau at once began what was to be a period of eighty-five years of distinguished research upon the Indians of North America. Its genesis was in the Act of March 3, 1879, which combined four government surveys into the U.S. Geological Survey, an agency in the Department of the Interior. The anthropological field work that these surveys had been performing did not belong in geology, and, as Powell stated, "in the act effecting this change it was provided that the ethnographic researches previously conducted by myself should be continued under the direction of the Smithsonian Institution and an appropriation was made therefor." Thus, ethnology became emancipated from geology within the government at least.

Powell knew firsthand what was happening to the American Indians, the wards of the U.S. Government, and he wanted to record their languages, myths, religions, arts, songs, and other parts of their culture before they disappeared from the face of the earth. His new bureau had virtually a virgin field before it. Even the science of anthropology itself was young, and some doubted that anthropology was a science at all.

Powell's ability as an organizer was soon felt, and the bureau, both through its own staff and through its collaborators, began to turn out important works of research in various branches of anthropology—archeology, linguistics, ethnology, and physical anthropology. And, combining field work with historical and bibliographic research, it continued to produce outstanding work until its absorption by the National Museum.

At the demise of the bureau, its staff was little larger than in the early days. Apparently, it never heard of Parkinson's Law. Its scientific staff included such eminent men as bureau chiefs William Henry Holmes (1902–10); Frederick Webb Hodge (1910–18); J. Walter Fewkes (1918–28); Matthew W. Stirling (1928–57); Frank H. H. Roberts, Jr. (1958–64); and Henry B. Collins (1964); and W J McGee, Henry Wetherbee Henshaw, Cyrus Thomas, James Mooney, Frank H. Cushing, Paul Radin, J. N. B. Hewitt, Truman Michelson, Francis La Flesche, John R. Swanton, William Duncan Strong, Julian H. Steward, Gordon R. Willey, William N. Fenton, John P. Harrington, William C. Sturtevant, and many others.

The work of the BAE combined field studies with historical research covering a broad area of archeology, linguistics, folklore, religion, music, and customs of the American Indians. The results appeared in a series of annual reports and book-length bulletins that formed an unparalleled scientific record of vanishing people. As the jacket of Neil Judd's book on the BAE stated, "These accounts salvaged many areas of history that were vanishing as quickly as—and often with—the older generations of Indians, who were dying without successors for their traditions, vocabularies, and knowledge." In all, the bureau published forty-eight of its finely illustrated annual reports and two hundred bulletins. One of the high marks of the bureau's achievement was the publication, in 1907 and 1910, of the two-volume *Handbook of the American Indians North of Mexico,* under the editorship of Frederick Hodge. It was a monumental work that has taken its place as a standard reference for students in many fields. Worthy of mention also are the *Handbook of American Indian Languages* (two volumes), *Handbook of the Indians of California,* and the *Handbook of South American Indians* (seven volumes).

In the early years, the bureau and the National Museum worked together. The museum developed its own Department of Anthropology, but its primary concern was to arrange displays of anthropological material for the visiting public and to build up reserve collections and make them available for study by those engaged in original research. The bureau, on the other hand, was not encumbered with museum functions and was required by law to turn over to the museum all its archeological and ethnological materials when study of them had been completed. The bureau's field work among the various tribes and at archeological sites yielded thousands of specimens in the nature of artifacts, skeletal remains, and cultural objects. The functions of the two units thus dovetailed rather than conflicted, with the result that the Smithsonian Institution became a world leader in the study of man on the earth. But gradually the natures of the work of the two began to appear indistinguishable, and by 1964 the more aggressive and persuasive anthropologists of the museum, taking advantage of a low ebb in the bureau's fortunes, were successful in effecting the merger, which one anthropologist characterized as an example of endocannibalism.

Claude Lévi-Strauss, in his address at the Smithson bicentennial celebration, referred to the BAE as one of the Smithsonian's

The Smithsonian has been well known for its museum activities, though the Institution is far more than a museum. Here, young people examine one of the exhibits during a field trip to the Smithsonian in 1898.

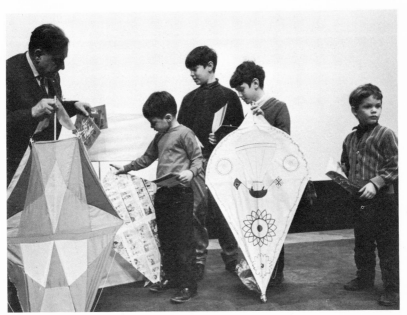

In recent years, the Smithsonian has expanded its activities to include many special events, one of which is an annual kite festival held on the Mall in Washington, D.C. A Smithsonian curator talks to a group of boys after a lecture on the use of kites in the development of aircraft.

Joseph Henry, physicist and organizer of the Smithsonian Institution, served as the first Secretary of the Institution from 1846 to 1878.

Spencer Fullerton Baird, a naturalist, has been called the father of the U.S. National Museum. He was Secretary of the Smithsonian from 1878 to 1887.

Samuel Pierpont Langley, astronomer and pioneer in aerodynamics, was the third Secretary of the Smithsonian Institution from 1887 to 1906. He established the Smithsonian Astrophysical Observatory and promoted the National Zoological Park.

Charles Doolittle Walcott, geologist and paleontologist, promoted aeronautics and the arts during his tenure as Secretary of the Smithsonian from 1907 to 1927.

Charles Greeley Abbot headed the Smithsonian Astrophysical Observatory before serving as Secretary of the Institution from 1928 to 1944. The National Gallery of Art was added to the bureaus of the Smithsonian during his administration.

Alexander Wetmore, a biologist and bird specialist, served as Secretary of the Smithsonian from 1945 to 1952. Two bureaus were added during his tenure: The National Air Museum and the Canal Zone Biological Area (now the Tropical Research Institute).

Leonard Carmichael, a psychologist, successfully promoted the construction of new Smithsonian buildings and the restructuring of its museum exhibits while serving as Secretary from 1953 to 1964.

S. Dillon Ripley, ornithologist, the eighth and present Secretary of the Smithsonian Institution, is a champion of museums for education and a proponent of the "new Smithsonian image."

Visitors view the pigmy hippopotamus at the National Zoological Park. (Photo by Leo Slaughter.)

Portraits of historic Americans are featured at the Smithsonian's newest gallery, the National Portrait Gallery. A portrait of President Calvin Coolidge is received by a former director of the gallery, Charles Nagel (right).

The Great Flight Cage and ramp at the National Zoological Park give visitors the opportunity to see the birds in a natural and spacious setting. (Photo by Mrs. Constance Warner.)

A sculptor from the Smithsonian Office of Exhibits completes a clay figure of a Congo chief for the Hall of Asian and African Cultures in the Museum of Natural History.

The collections of the National Museum of Natural History contain more than 50 million specimens of animals, plants, minerals, and human artifacts, the study of which is basic to man's understanding of the living world, past and present. A curator at the museum measures the leg bone of a fossil.

The Smithsonian's Radiation Biology Laboratory sponsors highly specialized research in photosynthesis, measurement of solar radiation, and carbon dating. Scientists in one project collect water samples from Tuborg Lake on Ellesmere Island, Northwest Territories, Canada. Analyses indicated that the salt water at the bottom of the lake has been trapped there for about 3,000 years.

The original Smithsonian Institution Building, known as the "Castle," was built between 1847 and 1855. A statue of Joseph Henry stands before the north front.

The Freer Gallery of Art, completed in 1921, houses one of the finest collections of Oriental art in the United States.

The National Gallery of Art was the gift of Andrew W. Mellon to house his collection of Renaissance art. It now boasts one of the finest collections in the United States. The dome of the Capitol can be seen in the distance.

The Arts and Industries Building was completed in 1881 to provide space for the exhibits received from the Philadelphia Centennial Exposition of 1876. It is about to begin a new career as the Smithsonian Exposition Hall.

The National Museum of Natural History, completed in 1909, housed the expanding collections of the U.S. National Museum. It now contains such priceless objects as the Hope Diamond and the Fénykövi Elephant.

The National Museum of History and Technology was opened to the public in January, 1964. It houses such unique exhibits as the original "Star-Spangled Banner," the *John Bull* locomotive, and the gowns of the First Ladies.

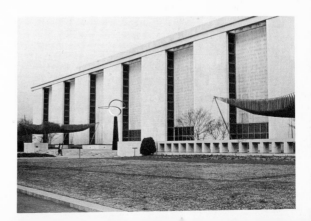

Research at the Smithsonian Astrophysical Observatory is integrated with the national space programs. The Baker-Nunn laser installation shown here is part of the equipment used at Mount Hopkins, Arizona, for optical stellar astronomy.

The Smithsonian Institution Traveling Exhibit Service reaches out to hundreds of other museums and art galleries throughout the country. With their teacher, children of Project Headstart from Arlington, Virginia, view a traveling exhibition of Tunisian mosaics.

greatest achievements and certainly a unique one of its kind. . . . We are primarily indebted to the Bureau for instituting standards of scholarship that still guide us, even though we but rarely succeed in attaining them. . . . I believe that all of us, together with its legal successor the Smithsonian Office of Anthropology, should seek in these achievements a living inspiration for the scientific task ahead of us.

And, indeed, much is ahead for anthropologists, for the study of man—into the dim eons of the future and as far back into the past as humans are able to delve—will never be finished. "The true science and study of man is man," wrote Pierre Charron centuries ago, and man is the most complex and elusive of subjects. The anthropologists will never run out of a job.

THE ASTROPHYSICAL OBSERVATORY

Astronomy was indigenous to the Smithsonian environment. John Quincy Adams had strongly advocated the establishment of an observatory. As a physicist, Joseph Henry was profoundly interested in astronomy. He had included it among prime Smithsonian concerns, and in many ways he laid the foundation for an observatory's ultimate establishment. Baird kept alive and promoted the observatory idea at the Smithsonian and, most importantly, in 1887 brought the astronomer Samuel P. Langley to the Institution as assistant secretary, perhaps feeling that it was time to start the Smithsonian pendulum swinging back toward the physical sciences.

The Astrophysical Observatory, truly a child of Langley, came into being in 1890 in a small wooden building (which is still standing) erected on the Smithsonian grounds directly south of the Smithsonian Building.* The next year it received

* Since its beginning, the observatory has had only four directors: Langley was succeeded by Charles G. Abbot in 1907; Abbot by Lloyd B. Aldrich in 1945; and Aldrich by Fred L. Whipple in 1955.

its first appropriation from Congress—a sum of $10,000. It was not an observatory in the usual sense, for it had no telescope to observe the stars in their courses; rather, Langley intended it to be a research center for what he called the "new astronomy" and particularly for solar physics. He had just completed his book *The New Astronomy* (Boston: Houghton Mifflin, 1888) in which he described the directions that the science was taking:

> The prime object of astronomy until lately has been to say *where* any heavenly body is, rather than what it is, but within the present generation a new branch of astronomy has arisen, which studies the heavenly bodies for what they are in themselves and in relation to ourselves. Its study of the sun, for instance, beginning with its external features, led to the inquiry as to what it was made of, and then to the finding of the unexpected relations it bore to the earth and to our daily lives on it, the conclusion being that in a physical sense it made us and recreates us, daily, and that the knowledge of the intimate ties which unite man with it brings results of a practical kind which a generation ago were hardly guessed at.

The first concern of the observatory's studies was to measure the intensity and characteristics of the infrared solar rays. By means of Langley's bolometer, which could record a millionth of a degree of temperature, it was possible to map the infrared bands of absorption caused by atmospheric water vapor, oxygen, and carbon dioxide, as well as several hundred infrared lines of absorption due to the sun's gases themselves. Another problem that received study was the determination of the proportion of the sun's heat that actually reached the earth and the amount dispersed in the outer atmosphere. Langley undertook to find out more accurately than was previously known the solar constant of radiation, that is, the amount of solar heat before it enters the atmosphere of the earth. Another question to be answered was whether the sun is a variable star, and, if so, how its variations affect the weather. Langley and his assistants attacked these problems with the aid of the facilities set up at the observatory, modest though they were, and achieved notable results. After 1900, the program included observations of the sun made simultaneously from two arrays of radiation using measuring equipment at several field stations located on high mountain peaks in Southwest Africa, Egypt, Chile, California, Arizona, and New Mexico.

In 1955, following the appointment of Dr. Fred L. Whipple as director, the observatory's headquarters were moved to Cambridge, Massachusetts, where its work, although administratively independent, became associated with that of the Harvard College Observatory. Its research programs were broadened, the solar-constant studies abandoned, the field stations phased out, and its energies directed toward a "broad dynamic program of astrophysical research with emphasis on what is now called space science." It was Whipple's aim to "embrace not only research in solar activity and its effects upon the earth, but also meteoritic studies and studies of the high atmosphere."

In anticipation of the launching of artificial satellites, the observatory was given the responsibility by the National Science Foundation and the National Academy of Sciences of organizing the so-called optical satellite-tracking program of the International Geophysical Year (IGY), which began in 1957. This task involved establishing a system for visual tracking, with stations all over the world manned by volunteer observers, together with a world-wide chain of twelve stations equipped with Baker-Nunn Schmidt-type telescopes to provide photographic tracking of artificial satellites. The whole satellite-tracking program was eminently successful and led to major new knowledge concerning the size and shape of the earth and the nature of its atmosphere. With continuing technical refinements, including laser satellite-tracking instruments, the twelve Baker-Nunn stations are still operating. Since 1959, they have been supported by NASA.

The observatory's staff at Cambridge now includes more than sixty-five scientists, most of them at the Ph.D. level, working on a great variety of astrophysical research problems. The projects are frequently supported by grants from and in cooperation with other agencies, government and nongovernment. Laboratory facilities provide for analysis of meteorites, for spectral measurements of atoms and molecules, and for optical studies. Current research at the observatory includes optical astronomy, radio astronomy, gamma-ray astronomy, stellar atmosphere and theoretical astrophysics, lunar and planetary studies, meteorites and cosmic dust, comets and meteors, and atomic and molecular physics.

The observatory's meteoritic science program is especially noteworthy. About 1962, this program was stepped up. The so-called Prairie Meteorite Network, consisting of sixteen automatic-camera stations, was set up in the midwestern United States to record meteors in flight and to determine their orbits and the probable site of a meteoritic fall from analysis of the film. In 1967, the network obtained good data on more than three hundred extremely bright meteors. In addition, radar observing stations for measuring the speed, trajectory, and flux of micrometeoroids entering the earth's atmosphere were established in several locations (first in cooperation with Harvard College Observatory and now independently); information concerning these particles is of vital interest to spacecraft designers preparing for the hazards of space flight.

The observatory's Project Celescope, a system of four telescope-television cameras designed to observe light in the far-ultraviolet region of the spectrum, was successfully launched into space aboard NASA's second Orbiting Astronomical Observatory on December 7, 1968. In space, the experiment package has functioned perfectly, returning observational data never before gathered from earth-bound observatories. Measurements of the far-ultraviolet brightness of several thousand stars, including parts of the constellations Draco, Lyra, Puppis, Taurus, and Orion, have been made. Celescope has recorded many stars in ultraviolet light that appear two or more magnitudes brighter than previously seen in visible light. An unexpected bonus of the system is its ability to observe and make systematic studies of the Lyman-alpha lines of hydrogen emission in the earth's outer atmosphere.

Most recently, the observatory has established a multipurpose facility at Mount Hopkins, about forty miles south of Tucson, Arizona. Although the observatory's camera stations have always provided astrophysical and geophysical data, this new site will become a center for advanced research in gamma-ray astronomy, stellar atmospheres, and similar topics. Already equipped with a Baker-Nunn camera and with a light collector for detecting gamma rays, by 1970 the Mount Hopkins Observatory is expected to have a 60-inch optical telescope.

These are but a few of the observatory's many research activities. They demonstrate, if nothing more, how in its eighty years the observatory has expanded its scientific horizons and today fills an important and unique role, a "place in the sun," if you will, in the government's gigantic over-all scientific programs.

CENTER FOR SHORT-LIVED PHENOMENA

More and more, the Smithsonian seeks to serve as a clearinghouse for the coordination of research and the gathering of information. One of the most recent examples of this trend is the Smithsonian Center for the Study of Short-Lived Phenomena, established on January 1, 1968, and planned as an international mobilization center for investigating rare or infrequent natural phenomena that might otherwise go scientifically unobserved. Examples of such phenomena are volcanic eruptions, earthquakes, tidal waves, meteorite falls, cyclones, fireballs, the birth of new islands, and sudden changes in biological and ecological systems. Whenever possible or appropriate, the center will coordinate actual investigations of the events, either by dispatching Smithsonian scientists to the scene or by alerting or assisting local scientists. The center is supervised by an interdisciplinary committee of Smithsonian scientists, chaired by Dr. Sidney Galler, the Institution's assistant secretary for Science, and is directed by Robert A. Citron, of the Smithsonian Astrophysical Observatory at Cambridge, Massachusetts, where the center's office activities are accommodated. The center now has about five hundred correspondents in seventy-five countries. During its first six months of operation, its scientists observed eighteen events, including five volcanic eruptions, four major earthquakes (greater than magnitude 7.0), four large fireballs, two major oil spills, and two important fish kills.

A case study for the center was furnished in the autumn of 1968 when hordes of gray squirrels were reported invading parts of the Great Smoky Mountains. Enlisting the help of biologists from the University of Maryland and the University of Georgia, scientists of the center were able to observe this mammalian phenomenon while it was still occurring in an effort to answer such questions as what causes squirrels to migrate; what specific event, or action, triggers the start of a migration; how do various and widely separated squirrel populations communicate the signal to migrate.

RADIATION BIOLOGY LABORATORY

In 1929, Secretary Abbot established within the Smithsonian Astrophysical Observatory a Division of Radiation and Organisms—a direct outgrowth of Langley and Abbot's studies of the solar spectrum—to investigate the "growth of plants under rigidly controlled physical and chemical conditions of soil, gases, temperature, humidity, intensity and color of light" and to cooperate with the Fixed Nitrogen Laboratory of the Department of Agriculture and with other scientists in related fields. Thus, the Smithsonian took on a new type of research, the objective being to discover the effects of radiation of various types and wavelengths upon living organisms, mainly plants.

At first, the program was financed chiefly by funds granted by the Research Corporation of New York, but in 1941 the work began to be supported by government appropriations as a continuing activity of the Smithsonian. A typical research project was the determination of the relative efficiencies of different wavelengths of light to promote photosynthesis in wheat.

For the most part, the division came to operate as an autonomous unit as its work more and more became separated from that of the mainstream of the observatory. In 1965, it was given independent status within the Institution, with its director reporting to the Secretary, and was renamed the Radiation Biology Laboratory. For four decades, this unit has been quietly carrying on research in the basement and in the north tower of the Smithsonian Building and in greenhouses on the premises. It has devised much ingenious and extremely delicate apparatus for its studies of plant growth. Its work is highly technical and is performed by a small staff. Year after year, the results of its studies have been published for the scientific world. Dr. Abbot liked to boast that the division "published the first accurate determination ever made of carbon-dioxide assimilation by a high order plant."

An interesting project in carbon dating was described in a 1967 report of the director, Dr. William H. Klein:

Field studies were made on Ellesmere Island, Northwest Territories, to determine the age of trapped seawater at the bottom of Lake Tuborg. Lake Tuborg, at the head of Greely Fiord, was formed when a glacier advanced across the fiord. At present, water of about 25 parts per million salinity lies in the bottom 60 meters while the upper 60 meters is fresh water. Temperature and salinity profiles indicate no complete mixing since the time of lake formation. Carbon-14/carbon-12 and carbon-13/carbon-12 ratios from analyses on dissolved bicarbonate from the lake and from a nearby fiord indicate that the saltwater in the bottom of the lake has been trapped there for about 3,000 years.

With its new status and name, the laboratory continues its emphasis upon three general research areas: regulatory biology (physiology of photomorphogenic responses and biochemical mechanisms), measurement of solar radiation (a continuation of the traditional work of Langley and Abbot), and radiocarbon dating (age determinations of samples).

TROPICAL RESEARCH INSTITUTE

During the construction of the Panama Canal, the area flooded included a large hill, the top of which projected above the water level to form Barro Colorado Island in Gatun Lake. In 1923, the Canal Zone governor, Jay Johnson Morrow, with commendable foresight, reserved the island for scientific purposes. In 1940, it was set aside permanently by Congress as a reserve to preserve in their original state the fauna, flora, and other natural features for study by scientists, particularly those from North, Central, and South America. The preserve's administration was assigned to a board of directors consisting of the secretaries of War, Agriculture, and the Interior, the Secretary of the Smithsonian Institution, the president of the National Academy of Sciences, and three eminent biologists. The zone remained under this imposing managment until 1946, when a Truman Administration plan for government reorganization placed it under the jurisdiction of the Smithsonian. It was named the Canal Zone Biological Area.

More or less jungle-covered, the island is the largest in Gatun Lake. It has a coastline of more than 25 miles and is about 3 miles wide, 3.5 miles long, and about 3,600 acres in area. The island is noted for its tropical monsoon forest and its wildlife population, including monkeys, neotropical birds, iguanas, jaguars, anteaters, and a myriad of insects—all existing in complete freedom from human interference, except, of course, for well-meaning researchers. A system of trails makes most of the island accessible, and in a small clearing overlooking Gatun Lake several buildings have been constructed to serve as laboratories, dormitories, a library, and a dining room for visiting scientists.

The station has never enjoyed affluent support. In its earlier days, it was maintained by contractual arrangements with other federal agencies and by fees subscribed by scientific and industrial institutions, such as the Eastman Kodak Company, which over a period of years has conducted studies on the island. But quite out of proportion to its financial resources, the Canal Zone program has yielded a large amount of scientific information, and several hundred publications based on Barro Colorado research have appeared. Emphasis has been particularly in such areas as bird and mammal observations, wildlife photography, entomology, and ecology.

In 1966, the name Canal Zone Biological Area was replaced by Smithsonian Tropical Research Institute, a change that reflected increasing activities and responsibilities and some broadening of scope. Federal funds allotted to the support of the agency's activities were gradually stepped up—in 1964 they totaled $138,890; in 1965, $179,640; in 1966, $213,000; and in 1967, $304,000—and it became possible to engage more staff members and to embark on new programs in research, education and training, and in certain aspects of conservation, such as oil pollution. The physical facilities were improved, and the institute began thinking in terms of extending its research beyond the American tropics to the Old World tropics. In 1967, it held a conference on tropical biology, at which it was resolved that

> an urgent need exists to begin long-term ecological studies now, especially in marine environments. Under present world conditions of exploding human populations and the limitations of the resources that support them, it is essential that any environmental manipulations as significant as the proposed Atlantic-Pacific sea-level canal be based on a comprehensive background of fundamental information.

Thus the concerns of the institute have become anything but parochial in concept.

Barro Colorado Island itself constitutes a unique combination of mature tropical forest and healthful laboratory surroundings: a combination that in the twenty-five years and more since it became a federal reserve has attracted hundreds of scientists and other visitors to its shores for serious study. Today, its potential as a focus for tropical biological and marine research in general is expanding, in consonance with the greater attention that is being devoted all over the world to the environmental sciences.

Office of Oceanography and Limnology

The science of oceanography is certainly not new; the word itself is probably about a century old, one lexicographer dating it "only from the commencement of the *Challenger* investigations."* Matthew Fontaine Maury, though often referred to as the father of modern oceanography and author of the first classic of modern marine science, *The Physical Geography of the Sea,* which appeared in 1855, probably

---

* The voyage of *H. M. S. Challenger,* 1872–76. Reports on the scientific results of this expedition appeared in forty volumes from 1880 to 1895.

never used the term. By the mid-1890's, however, the word was in common scientific use, and the Smithsonian annual reports for 1895 and 1898 each carried an article on oceanography.

The Smithsonian has, of course, been engaged in the study of marine biology ever since the days of Secretary Baird. Its first extensive oceanographic collections, to which it fell heir, originated in the U.S. Exploring Expedition of 1838–40. The years when Baird was head of the U.S. Fish Commission saw several oceanographic expeditions launched under its aegis. Whole books have been written on the voyages of the *Albatross, Fish Hawk,* and other vessels sent out at various times by the commission for deep-sea exploration. The scientific results of these expeditions are inestimable, and the collections dredged and brought back by them, not only of fishes from many parts of the globe, but also of other forms of marine life, have been an almost inexhaustible source of zoological study at the National Museum and elsewhere.

Oceanography received considerable stimulus through the world-wide programs of the International Geophysical Year. This 1957–58 undertaking represented an area where international cooperation operated productively. Scientists and the general public began to be more acutely aware that the oceans might someday prove to be the last frontier for the exploitation of natural resources and that knowledge about them was crucial. The eminent oceanographer Athelstan Spilhaus, in a 1964 paper entitled "Oceanography's Future," wrote, "Oceanography is not a single scientific discipline, but an adventure where any discipline or combination of disciplines may be brought to bear and focus on understanding and using the sea and all that's in it."

Shortly after the International Geophysical Year ended, the Smithsonian began to corral its scattered oceanographic activities to give them a focus and in August, 1962, appointed Dr. I. Eugene Wallen as assistant director of the National

Museum for Oceanography. The government had set up an interdepartmental National Oceanography Program, and the Smithsonian keyed its activities to this program, at the same time realizing that traditionally its marine operations had been largely oriented to systematics and concerned principally with collecting marine natural-history objects to determine the kinds, distributions, and populations of organisms and sediments in the world's oceans.

As a part of its involvement in the national program, the Institution organized and set up the Smithsonian Oceanographic Sorting Center (SOSC), providing a unique service to the scientific community by receiving, sorting, recording, and distributing marine biological and geological specimens. The magnitude of this involvement is evidenced by the nearly eighty U.S. oceanographic vessels that are gathering marine specimens, many of which may end up at the Smithsonian Institution. Not only do Smithsonian scientists participate in expeditions to all oceans, but also, as the legal repository for collections made with federal funds, the Smithsonian receives collections from the Coast Guard, the National Science Foundation, the Geological Survey, the Bureau of Sports Fisheries and Wildlife, the Bureau of Commercial Fisheries, the U.S. Navy, the Army Coastal Engineering Research Center, the Atomic Energy Commission, the Public Health Service, the Department of State, and other agencies and universities. Indeed, this service has developed into quite an operation. Its quantitative output was described in a 1968 report of the director:

Since SOSC began operations, 39,127 samples of marine organisms and sediments have been received. From 15,573 of these samples, 19,022,934 specimens, 6,668 unsorted lots, and 277,-895 cc. of an estimated 2,000,000 shell fragments have been sorted to date. During the year, 3,484,354 specimens were sorted. Shipments made totaled 310, including 1,792 unsorted lots and 17,128 sorted lots, the latter containing 912,802 specimens. A total of 1,300 shipments of marine specimens have been sent during the five and one-half years of SOSC existence. These shipments included 6,668 unsorted lots and 58,838 sorted lots, the latter including 6,747,688 whole specimens and 277,895 cc. of shell fragments.

In June, 1966, all these oceanographic operations were elevated to a full-fledged office—the Office of Oceanography and Limnology—and placed under the supervision of the assistant secretary for Science. The services and functions of this new office cut across the work of several Smithsonian bureaus and departments. It serves as a clearinghouse for all aquatic research of Smithsonian staff members, maintains liaison with ocean-going vessels and scientists collecting biological materials, represents the Institution on various committees and councils concerned with oceanography and limnology, brings the Smithsonian's plans and needs in hydrobiology to the attention of scientists and administrators elsewhere, and operates the sorting center aforementioned.

The office has also become involved with the development of programs supported through the use of P.L. 480 funds, the currencies that exist in a number of countries through the sale of U.S. commodities. Through an appropriation by Congress, the Smithsonian has been able to carry on a number of programs of direct benefit to U.S. interests. For example, the office, through the use of foreign currencies, has responded to the need for facilities in the Mediterranean area similar to those of the Oceanographic Sorting Center in Washington, D.C., and has established the Mediterranean Marine Sorting Center (MMSC) at the Institut National Scientifique et Technique d'Océanographie et de Pêche, in Salambaw, Tunisia. This center, offering its services to marine scientists of all countries, especially to those in the Mediterranean area, began operations in November, 1966.

Another program worth noting is the current study of the role of the Suez Canal as a pathway for fish migration between the Red Sea and the Mediterranean. Through the use of funds in Israel and in cooperation with Hebrew University in Jerusalem, Smithsonian scientists have demonstrated that more than 150 species have migrated from the Red Sea into the Mediterranean; the reverse route, however, is much less traveled, with only one or two species known to have made the migration.

OFFICE OF ECOLOGY

The Office of Ecology, among the newer ventures of the Smithsonian, was given official status in 1965 as a unit of the National Museum. Dr. Helmut K. Buechner was named its director. Here again the functions of the office cut across divisional lines, and it soon attained autonomous status similar to that of the Office of Oceanography and Limnology under the Secretariat. The Office of Ecology represents the Smithsonian's response to the world-wide accentuated concern with environmental biology. Its prime objectives as stated are "to contribute to theory in population biology and ecosystem science" and "to provide information essential to the Federal Government in the evolution of society in the critical years ahead."

One of the first of the office's projects was to develop a preserve for ecosystem biology on the west shore of Chesapeake Bay, conveniently accessible to scientific and educational institutions in the Washington-Baltimore area. It was envisioned as an "open-end consortium" in which institutions such as the Johns Hopkins University, the University of Maryland, the National Institutes of Health, and others would conduct cooperative research and education in ecology. The 700-acre preserve is planned to include both natural and controlled environments in a number of habitats and facilities for marine research. The program includes field and laboratory studies of vegetation change, social behavior of mammals, estuarine ecology, and the consequences of environmental manipulations.

The office has made itself internationally useful by integrating with the International Biological Program (IBP) which is strongly oriented toward ecosystem ecology with a view toward broadening the productivity base for human populations. In a recent Smithsonian report, Dr. Buechner described this cooperative venture:

> The Office of Ecology constitutes a focal point for staff participation in this program, and the ecology program is integrated wherever possible with the several sections of the IBP. The Smithsonian, in conjunction with the IBP, is concerned with the development of the international program in terrestrial conservation, one of the objectives of which is to create a network of nature reserves. A major Smithsonian contribution to this will be in helping with the inventory of the biological components and general descriptions of the ecosystems preserved.

AMERICAN STUDIES

Late in 1965, a Department of American Studies was set up in the Museum of History and Technology, with Dr. Wilcomb E. Washburn, formerly the museum's curator of political history, as chairman. In 1968, since it was concerned with research and education in a noncuratorial way, the unit shed its allegiance to the museum and became one more of the appendages attached to the Office of the Secretary—another instance of the trend toward programmatic organization within the Institution.

The chief function of this operation is to conduct an American studies program in cooperation with universities throughout the country. It provides a link between university graduate programs in American history and related studies and the Smithsonian's own resources of personnel, objects, manuscripts, and books. The program includes seminars, conferences, reading and research courses with individual staff members, and thesis direction for graduate students. The Smithsonian is not a degree-granting institution, but graduate students involved in the program receive academic credit from the participating universities. The program is expected to open up many little-explored areas of research, particularly in cultural history, to doctoral students in American universities. The end result will be to make museum resources in the United States better known and more effectively utilized by scholars.

Woodrow Wilson Center

A long-advocated international center for scholars, to be created as the nation's memorial to Woodrow Wilson, approached the point of realization in October, 1968, when President Johnson signed the Woodrow Wilson Memorial Act of 1968, following seven years' work and study by the Woodrow Wilson Memorial Commission established by Congress. It was the consensus of Congress that the establishment of such a center "would be consonant with the purposes of the Smithsonian Institution," and accordingly the Act allocated the center to the care of the Smithsonian, its immediate maintenance and administration to be the responsibility of a board of trustees of fifteen members, including the Smithsonian Secretary. The site where the center is to be built lies north of Pennsylvania Avenue between the National Archives Building and the proposed Market Square. It is contemplated that funds necessary to construct the center will be appropriated by Congress but that operating funds will be sought from private sources and will be sufficient to provide a sizable annual income in order that the center be "freed of the annual Federal budget cycle and divested altogether of any suggestion of political influence." The proposed program will revolve around scholarly endeavor in fields most closely associated with Wilson's career and interests: American government and politics, the legislative process, international law and organization, the peaceful settlement of international disputes, and social ethics.

The center is conceived on a grand and dignified scale befitting the character, spirit, and accomplishments of the man it will memorialize. "A Woodrow Wilson Memorial constructed as a center to which scholars would come from all parts of the world," Secretary Ripley has stated, "would unmistakably embody man's unending quest for knowledge and inspire young people in this country to seek that understanding of our fellow man which still is so elusive." The center embodies a large hope and a great potential, and Americans await its fulfillment, again under the protecting aegis of Smithson's institution.

VII

Galleries and the Arts

A gallery of art was inherent in the Act of 1846 that established the Smithsonian, for the Act specified that all objects of art and natural history belonging to the United States in Washington were to be transferred to the Institution. Among the first of such objects was a group of art works that had been assembled by John Varden, a Washington citizen who had established a small museum in the capital in 1829. His collection became a part of the art holdings of the National Institute and was exhibited in the Patent Office Building before it was moved to the Smithsonian in 1862. Though the collection was slowly augmented, it occupied little exhibition space and was consigned to a small area on the second floor of the Smithsonian Building. Then in the Smithsonian fire of January, 1865, most of the collection went up in flames, including the Indian paintings of John Mix Stanley and Charles Bird King. All that remained of Smithsonian art were a few pieces that had been placed elsewhere in the building.

The Smithsonian's concern with art was not extinguished with the fire, however, but it smoldered for a good while before it was slowly and surely rekindled, as wealthy men began giving their art collections to the nation. Today the Smithsonian's complex of art galleries devoted both to the visual and the performing arts has helped to make Washington one of the world's great art centers.

The National Collection of Fine Arts

For about thirty years after the fire, most of the art objects received by the Institution were turned over to the Library of Congress or to the Corcoran Gallery of Art in Washington. The Centennial Exposition of 1876 in Philadelphia helped in some degree to renew an interest in developing the art collections, for although the show's principal emphasis was industrial, the thousands of Americans who visited it must have been impressed by the carefully selected art exhibited by the participating countries. Five "magnificent pictures" were lent by Queen Victoria herself, and J. S. Ingram, one of the chroniclers of the exposition, recorded that "there was always a dense crowd around" two of William Powell Frith's paintings, *The Railway Station* and *The Marriage of the Prince of Wales*. "Their hard, honest, careful realism was instantly understood by the multitude."

Secretary Langley was particularly sensitive to the need for a national art collection and remarked, "The scientific side of the Institution's activities has been in the past so much greater than its aesthetic that it is well to recall the undoubted fact that it was intended by Congress to be a curator of art, and that this function has never been forgotten, though often in abeyance." But the development of an art gallery lagged, and it was not until 1896 that the material deposited in the Corcoran Gallery and the Library of Congress was recalled and a large room in the east wing of the Smithsonian Building was fitted up for prints and an art library.

It is difficult to determine all the reasons for this cultural lag. Congress, during the nineteenth century, was certainly far from art-minded, and the country as a whole was more intrigued with its canals and railroads and more concerned with westward expansion and getting rich than it was with art. Richard Rathbun in his history of the National Gallery of Art remarked that although "Congress directed the establishment of a museum and a gallery of art . . . art in its highest sense was neither helped nor encouraged, and whatever was acquired was mostly inferior in character." Barely enough art collections were received by the gallery to fan the fire, though a few of considerable importance did come, such as the Catlin Indian paintings.

Then too, Washington was still a provincial city, with no ambitions to become an art center. "It contrasted sharply," observed Constance McLaughlin Green in *Washington Capital City, 1879–1950* (Princeton, N.J.: Princeton University Press, 1963), "with the catholicity of taste and many-faceted artistic talents to be found in European capitals. Henry James implied that Washington's self-absorbed conversation at best touched very lightly on the creative arts." She quoted an anonymous English visitor as saying that the city had "no influence over the arts and letters of the American people. The day is infinitely distant and in all probability will never come at all when every American artist, author, dramatist, and musician will turn instinctively toward Washington."

Into such an atmosphere the needed stimulus finally came, and the matter of a national art collection was brought to a culmination by a bequest of paintings from Mrs. Harriet Lane Johnston, James Buchanan's niece, who had served as his First Lady just before the Civil War. Mrs. Johnston had assembled at her home in Washington paintings and other historical objects of some value. At her death in 1903, she left this entire collection to the Corcoran Gallery of Art with the stipulation that should the U.S. Government ever establish in Washington a national gallery of art, the collection should be turned over to it and become its absolute property. Under these conditions, the Corcoran Gallery declined the bequest, with the result that the following year, by a court decree, the art collections of the Smithsonian Institution were "designated and established" as the National Gallery of Art. Accordingly, the Harriet Lane Johnston collection—thirty-one pieces in all including paintings, marbles, and miscellaneous articles—was delivered to the Smithsonian Building and installed in the reception rooms and the Secretary's office. Represented among the paintings were works ascribed to John Constable, Sir Thomas Lawrence, Bernardino Luini, Sir Joshua Reynolds, and George Romney. "Valuable as were the paintings," wrote Richard Rathbun, "the real gain was in the stimulus given to art . . . in the example set that the Government might be trusted as a custodian of art for the people."

The Johnston collection was at first exhibited in the lecture room of what is now the Art and Industries Building, but the completion of the new National Museum building (now the Natural History Building), portions of which were opened to the public in 1910, provided space for an art hall, which began to draw increasing public attention to the Smithsonian collection. The gallery had already attracted gifts from collectors following the example of Harriet Lane Johnston. The largest, that of Charles L. Freer in 1906, eventually became a separate gallery. Among other benefactors since then have been William T. Evans, Ralph Cross Johnson, Henry Ward Ranger, John Gellatly, and Laura and Natalie Barney. The most recent very large gift was a collection of 102 contemporary paintings from the firm of S. C. Johnson & Sons. In 1969, this collection toured the world as "Art: U.S.A.: Now."

Until 1920, the gallery's status was that of a department in the National Museum, but in that year, by congressional authority, it was made an independent bureau of the Smithsonian with its own appropriation. William Henry Holmes was the first director. Even then, the gallery was suffering growing pains, accommodated as it was in a building primarily devoted to purposes other than art. Several attempts were made to promote provision of a new building for the gallery's sole use, but for nearly half a century it had no success in obtaining more adequate space for its growing collections, for exhibit, study, or storage. W. P. True, in his book on the Smithsonian, quotes Dr. Holmes on the frustrations that surrounded the gallery:

> The story . . . from its beginning nearly a century ago is the record of the prolonged struggle of the art idea for national recognition, for a place in the serious consideration of the American people. . . . The Smithsonian has harbored the dream of a gallery of art, but art has been in the shadow of diversified scientific activities and in the deeper shadow of the all-absorbing material interests of a rapidly developing nation. Growth of the collections through gratuitous contributions, even, is embarrassed by the almost complete exhaustion of space for the reception and display of all save accessions of very limited extent.

Late in the 1930's, an architects' competition was held for a Smithsonian gallery building; the first prize of $7,500 was won by Gottlieb Eliel Saarinen, but the building he designed was never erected.

By the mid-1960's, it was apparent that Congress was not about to authorize a new building for the national collection, and so the Smithsonian accepted a proffered substitute, the historic Old Patent Office Building vacated by the Civil Service Commission. The building was thoroughly renovated, and in May, 1968, the gallery moved out of the Natural History Building and for the first time in its history enjoyed elbow room, ample curatorial facilities, and the attention it deserved.

In 1937, the bureau was renamed the National Collection of Fine Arts (NCFA) after Andrew Mellon's gift established the great Mellon Gallery under the Smithsonian, for which the name National Gallery of Art was purloined. Accompanying the change in name came a charge from Congress for the NCFA to "foster . . . a growing appreciation of art" and "to encourage the development of contemporary art and to effect the widest distribution and cultivation in matters of such art." Perhaps what the congressmen had in mind was an American equivalent of the Luxembourg Gallery in France or the Tate Gallery in England. Whatever their intention, the result has been emphasis on contemporary art in the gallery's exhibitions, accessions, and programs.

Over the years, the National Collection of Fine Arts has sought to fulfill the congressional mandate in its widest sense and has interpreted its functions as follows:

1. Encouraging the development of native American art and craft;
2. Promoting the appreciation of art on a national scale and sponsoring traveling exhibits within the United States and internationally;
3. Providing a repository for government-sponsored art, with special concern for the conservation of such works;
4. Lending to government agencies, the White House, U.S. embassies, and similar groups;
5. Representing the U.S. Government in matters of art;
6. Encouraging the study of art and supplying information on art for students and scholars from the United States and abroad;
7. Planning for the creation of a national study and archival center.

These functions are translated into the gallery's special and continuing programs and activities. In particular, the NCFA every year holds a number of major exhibitions designed to demonstrate current happenings in the world of art, particularly American, as well as to feature "modern old masters."

Exhibitions held during the period 1966–68 included *Eleven Pop Artists,* a show of prints by eleven contemporary artists; *Paul Manship Memorial Exhibition 1885–1966,* featuring the work of this great American sculptor; *The United States at the 1966 Venice Biennale Exhibition,* featuring four artists from this prestigious international event; *Stanton Macdonald-Wright,* a retrospective show of the work of this pioneer abstractionist; *The Graphic Art of Mary Cassatt,* a definitive collection of the artist's etchings and lithographs; and *The Drawings of Jasper Johns.*

The gallery also operates the International Art Program, which originated in the U.S. Information Service but was moved to the Smithsonian in 1965. One of IAP's major responsibilities is American representation at the large recurring international exhibitions, most notably the biennials of Venice and São Paulo. Though sometimes controversial—a natural characteristic of exhibitions of this type—IAP-sponsored exhibitions have won prizes at many of these events, including the Santiago Print Biennial, the First India Triennial, the Fifth Biennial of Paris, and the São Paulo Biennial of 1967. The agency organized a traveling print workshop that was sent to Pakistan for a 3-month period and has sent exhibitions to Germany, India, Chile, and other countries. Typical of its educational activities were a 1966 symposium on the subject "How Should American Art be Presented Abroad?" and a special 6-evening film series on "The History of the Art of the American Film."

The NCFA is under the general surveillance of the Smithsonian Art Commission, which is composed of up to twenty-five art experts from outside the Smithsonian and the Institution's Secretary, who is the Commission's ex officio secretary. The group meets at least twice a year to review works of art offered to the National Collection of Fine Arts and to recommend acceptance or rejection.

The Freer Gallery

It may be said that the National Collection of Fine Arts was the parent of all later Smithsonian art galleries. It was certainly the inspiration for the Freer Gallery of Art.

Charles Lang Freer was a Detroit industrialist who made his money in the railroad and foundry business. In 1900, at the age of fifty-four, he was able to retire from active business, and he devoted the rest of his life to his hobby, collecting art. He traveled widely and became an expert, particularly in the classic arts of China, though he never claimed to be a scholar. He had, it is recorded, a "sincere and deep regard for the truth, for right proportion and exact understanding of the fine arts."

Freer first offered his art collection to the Smithsonian on January 3, 1905. His gift was almost as startling as that of James Smithson, for no one had presented an art gallery to the U.S. Government before. The following December, Freer went directly to President Theodore Roosevelt, who, after some prodding, convinced the Smithsonian regents that the offer was a superb opportunity. Nevertheless, it was more than a year before the regents accepted, and the formal deed of gift was not signed until May 5, 1906.

The gift included Freer's entire art collection, which he had built up over a period of twenty-three years and which at that time amounted to 2,250 objects, plus $500,000 for a building to house the collection.* In addition, Freer created an endowment fund whose income was to be used "for the study of the civilization of the Far East," for additions to the Oriental collections, and for other related activities that he

* Freer continued adding to the collection, so that by the time of his death in 1919, when the gift took effect, the collection included 9,500 objects.

wished carried on free from congressional appropriations. Naturally his art collection reflected his own interests in the arts of the Orient and in the arts of the West, as represented by a few painters he had collected, among whom were James McNeill Whistler (Freer was his friend and patron), Thomas W. Dewing, Childe Hassam, Winslow Homer, Gari Melchers, Albert Pinkham Ryder, John Singer Sargent, and John Henry Twachtman.

The building for the Freer collection was begun in 1916 and completed in the spring of 1921, a year and a half after Freer's death. It was opened to the public on May 2, 1923. Freer had retained the right to keep the collection in his possession during his lifetime and to add to it. He had a hand in the design of his gallery, which he wanted erected on the Smithsonian grounds. He wanted the building "constructed and equipped . . . with special regard for the convenience of students and others desirous of an opportunity for uninterrupted study of the objects embraced hereunder." He provided for a continuing high degree of selectivity by stipulating that there would be no loans to or from the collection or additions to it by gift. The government agreed to the terms and to maintain the building and collections at public expense.

The Freer Gallery has been described under such glowing epithets as "the jewel of the Smithsonian," "a model museum," "the scholar's museum," and it is eminently deserving of them. Its staff is small and professional; its standards are high; its job, expertly done. With some effort, the gallery has been able to isolate itself from much of the pressure that characterizes other parts of government, even the Smithsonian. It takes a dim view of public relations efforts, preferring to offer its truly precious wares to the public elegantly, perhaps austerely, but without fanfare. Its scholarly works are published in monographs that will last the ages. The gallery's quality was well described in a letter received by the museum's director a few years ago:

The gallery proved a pleasant refuge on this snowy afternoon. . . . it is unusual today to find an art museum that is quiet, tasteful, restful; that has objects so good that it is unnecessary to call attention to them by the techniques of the department store. No trace of "togetherness" . . . no clatter, no commotion, only an extraordinary variety of works of art quietly displayed in a building that is handsome without being obtrusive. I hope that it will never lose this character.

As a result of its solicitous adherence to Freer's trust, which was well founded, the Freer Gallery has developed into one of the world's two or three great centers of Oriental art. The Oriental collections comprise about 4,000 Chinese objects, 2,000 Japanese, and 3,000 from the Near East and India. Chinese bronzes, Chinese paintings, and Chinese ceramics bulk large in the collections. In the Japanese category, the Freer is probably strongest in painting and ceramics. In Near East art, its strength is in Persian miniatures and early Persian metalwork. In accordance with Freer's wish, the gallery purchased no further Western works after his death but still holds the approximately 1,500 works of American art collected by him during his lifetime, including Whistler's famous Peacock Room. The Freer collections are widely known for their quality and scope and attract scholars from all over the world. The gallery also contains a fine reference library of some 35,000 volumes.

In addition to its gallery activities, the Freer maintains a technological chemical laboratory that carries on a program of research on the materials and methods "of the ancient craftsmen in Asia with the twofold goal of broadening knowledge of the history of technology and of increasing the Gallery's ability to protect and preserve the objects in the collections." It has become a prototype for other American art-conservation centers. The Freer also maintains a studio for the conservation and restoration of Oriental paintings and works of art and for many years has been the center of this unique activity, which has benefited not only the Freer collections but also those of other museums, institutions, and individuals here and abroad. The studio has aided in keeping alive the highly specialized and rapidly vanishing skills necessary to the proper care of Chinese and Japanese paintings.

THE NATIONAL GALLERY OF ART

Just thirty years after the Freer gift, another industrialist, Andrew W. Mellon, a wealthy Pittsburgh banker and Secretary of the Treasury under Presidents Warren G. Harding, Calvin Coolidge, and Herbert Hoover, responded in a magnificent way to his philanthropic conscience by founding the National Gallery of Art. Like Freer, he did not live to see his building completed and opened. Like Freer, he had spent many years collecting art, and his assemblage of Renaissance art was fabulous. On December 31, 1936, he gave to the American people his entire collection of paintings and sculpture, over $15 million for a building to house and exhibit the collection, and an endowment fund for the salaries of executive officers and the acquisition of additional art works. The gallery was to be a bureau of the Smithsonian Institution but administered by its own board of trustees. Congress gave the museum official blessing on March 24, 1937. The building was opened to the public four years later.

Mellon envisioned his philanthropy as the genesis of one of the great art galleries of the world, and his dream has come true. His own gift consisted of about 115 paintings dating from the thirteenth to the eighteenth century, some 20 Italian Renaissance sculptures, and a number of American paintings. Though not great in quantity, the collection was of superb quality and commanded the highest respect. Lord Duveen described it as "the finest in the universe." "Princely but not prodigal," said another commentator. As the donor had intended, other collectors were inspired to augment the Mellon nucleus, and over the years important gifts have come from Samuel H. Kress, Joseph E. Widener, Chester Dale, Lessing J. Rosenwald, the Edgar William Garbisches, and many others. "Never before," John Walker, director of the National Gallery, once said, "has such a magnificent collection been assembled in so short a time."

One of the gallery's particular charges is the Index of American Design, a collection of watercolor renderings of the popular arts in the United States from before 1700 to 1900. The collection is available to artists, designers, manufacturers, museums, libraries, and art schools for study.

It is a surprise to many people to learn that the National Gallery of Art is a part of the Smithsonian. The gallery is in fact autonomous and separately administered with its own board of trustees and its own federal budget. But Mellon, who had served on the Smithsonian Art Commission and was a member of the Smithsonian Establishment while Secretary of the Treasury, apparently was familiar with the fundamentals of the Institution and thought that the gallery would benefit from its protection. The Secretary of the Smithsonian is an ex officio member of the gallery's board of trustees. Dr. Abbot, who was Smithsonian Secretary when the National Gallery was founded, related that Mellon "felt that the unique governmental relations of the Smithsonian Institution, its freedom from political interference and all suspicion of graft, its close association with cultural institutions the world over, altogether made the Smithsonian the ideal repository for the gift he contemplated." In accepting the Mellon gift, Congress agreed that the government would provide for the upkeep, administrative expenses, and operating costs of the gallery. In 1968, these expenses totaled more than $3 million.

The gallery draws more than 1.5 million visitors a year. In addition to its permanent exhibitions and its twenty or so special exhibitions shown annually, it carries on related programs—special tours, lectures, publications, conferences, a slide-lending service, and a traveling exhibition service. The gallery's concerts, performed by its own orchestra on Sunday evenings in the east garden court, have become a popular part of the musical life of the capital. The gallery maintains a sizable art library, and its staff conducts research and publishes its findings.

THE NATIONAL PORTRAIT GALLERY

Agitation for a national portrait gallery began at least fifty years ago, as evidenced by a statement that appeared in the Smithsonian annual report for 1921:

In January, 1919, a number of patriotic citizens and patrons of art realized that if the United States was to have a pictorial record of the World War it would be necessary to take immediate steps. A number of the distinguished leaders of America and of the Allied Nations were approached and their consent secured for the painting of their portraits by prominent American artists. With the indorsement of the Smithsonian Institution as custodian of the National Gallery of Art [now the National Collection of Fine Arts], the American Federation of Arts, and the American Mission to Negotiate Peace, then in session at Paris, the National Portrait Committee came into being for the purpose of carrying out this idea and thus initiating and establishing in Washington a National Portrait Gallery.

This scheme apparently was the beginning of the national portrait collection. The committee, which numbered among its members such prominent citizens as Mrs. E. H. Harriman, J. Pierpont Morgan, and Henry C. Frick, achieved notable success, for in May, 1921, an exhibit of twenty portraits completed under the plan was held in the National Museum quarters assigned to the gallery, and these were later shown in a number of cities throughout the country under the auspices of the American Federation of Arts.

With this small collection as a nucleus, the number of portraits slowly increased, but it was many years before the gallery was accorded separate identity within the Smithsonian organization. The sentiment was often expressed that the United States ought to have a national portrait gallery comparable to that of the British, and the Smithsonian Art Commission took the matter to heart. One of its prime recommendations was that such a gallery be separated from its parent organization, the National Collection of Fine Arts, and be set up as a separate bureau of the Smithsonian. Congress followed the recommendation and set up an advisory National Portrait Gallery Commission to oversee the development of the new bureau. The separation of the two galleries, though it seemed to some illogical, was based primarily on the inherent differences between their collections. The National Collection of Fine Arts is an art museum first and foremost, whereas the National Portrait Gallery is a history-oriented museum and as such must contain many likenesses and other material that might find no legitimate place in the NCFA. Also, inasmuch as the National Portrait Gallery must appeal for donations of likenesses as well as of money, it was felt that the gallery should be a primary institution in its own right, not simply a department of a larger agency.

The job of the National Portrait Gallery Commission is to promote

the administration, development, and utilization of the National Portrait Gallery, including the acquisition of material of high quality. . . . As a group and as individuals, its members are responsible for encouraging distinguished gifts of funds, portraits, statuary, and other items that would enhance the value and significance of the gallery.

The enabling act for the National Portrait Gallery was signed by President John F. Kennedy on April 26, 1962. It specified that the gallery "shall function as a free public museum for the exhibition and study of portraiture and statuary depicting men and women who have made significant contributions to the history, development, and culture of the people of the United States and of the artists who created such portraiture and statuary." Charles Nagel, a St. Louis museum man, was named director, and he set to work organizing and planning against the day when the gallery's new quarters in the renovated Old Patent Office Building would be ready. The move was made early in 1968 from the gallery's temporary quarters in the Arts and Industries Building, and the gallery opened on the evening of October 5 with a glittering black-tie ceremony. At last, the United States had a National Portrait Gallery worthy of the name.

The commission has adopted ground rules for the admission of portraits to the National Portrait Gallery. The criterion of admission, it says, shall be the national significance of the person portrayed and, to a lesser degree, the competence and skill of the artist. Selection shall be made without bias toward any political party, race, or creed; nor shall faults of character, even of the most severe nature, be grounds for exclusion. In general, the point of reference shall be inclusion of the candidate in the *Dictionary of American Biography*.

Thus the gallery hopes to acquire the best portraits available, originals from life whenever possible, replicas or copies if necessary. The selection will be made by the commission acting upon the recommendation of a subcommittee on admission and of the professional staff of the gallery. Admission will be by a majority two-thirds vote of the commission and will be confirmed by the Board of Regents of the Smithsonian Institution. It is further stipulated that no likeness of any person who has been dead less than ten years shall be exhibited, with the exception of that of a President of the United States and his wife.

The gallery is planned to be a study center as well as an

art museum. It contemplates a program for collecting extensive biographical, archival, and iconographic materials, assembling a skilled and ample staff of librarians and scholars to engage in research and assist visitors, and publishing its researches. Its objective is to become a first-rate resource for scholars in American history and biography as well as a showplace for the likenesses of distinguished, or even notorious, Americans.

THE JOHN F. KENNEDY CENTER FOR THE PERFORMING ARTS

It has been suggested that the idea of a cultural center for the city of Washington began with George Washington himself, when in 1789 he commissioned Pierre Charles L'Enfant to plan a federal city that would be a cultural and civic center for the nation. Scarcely anyone would claim that this objective has been fully realized in the nearly two ensuing centuries, but a great milestone was reached in 1958 when the National Cultural Center was established by act of Congress as a bureau of the Smithsonian. Its rather pretentious name was changed in January, 1964, to the John F. Kennedy Center for the Performing Arts to memorialize the former President, whose life and work seemed so thoroughly consonant with its purposes.

The center is national in the sense that the American people have been given the opportunity to participate in its creation as well as in its use. The initial legislation authorized a federal appropriation of $15.5 million, provided matching funds were raised by the public in five years. This time limit was subsequently extended to eight years. A nationwide appeal for funds was successful, and ground was broken for the building just eight years after the first authorization became a law. The center's trustees were also granted authority to issue revenue bonds to the Secretary of the Treasury, payable from revenues accruing to them, to a value not greater than

$15.4 million, to be used for the construction of underground parking facilities.

The center will certainly be a cultural boon for the capital region, which has never had adequate facilities to accommodate the performing arts or enough cohesive community zeal to bring them into being. But to what extent it will fulfill its objective as a national institution, serving a broader public less parochially than do the cultural centers of many of our cities, remains to be seen. Its development will depend on management, public demands, and sustained financial support. It is salutary, perhaps, to recall that even science was once not considered a proper concern of government. That concept has changed, and now even music, drama, opera, poetry, festivals, and Terpsichore herself are stepping onto the dais with science as worthy of the taxpayer's dollar. It is of interest to note that Thomas Jefferson, in the early years of the Republic, not only was one of the few who saw science as a proper interest of government but also possessed a civilized and prescient regard for the arts. In a letter to James Madison in 1795, he wrote: "I am an enthusiast on the subject of the arts. But it is an enthusiasm of which I am not ashamed, as its object is to improve the taste of my countrymen, to increase their reputation, to reconcile to them the respect of the world, and procure them its praise." The American Muse has only begun to come into her own, and there will no doubt be a long period of evolution toward the realization by every man that enjoyment and involvement in things of the spirit are a part of his constitutional birthright, the right to the pursuit of happiness.

Like the National Gallery of Art, the John F. Kennedy Center, though a bureau of the Smithsonian, is administered by a separate board of trustees comprised of forty-five members—thirty general and fifteen ex officio members, the latter including the Secretary of the Smithsonian. The center also enjoys the support of an auxiliary group called the Friends of the Kennedy Center, whose membership at present is about one thousand. They represent the various performing arts throughout the country and in general endeavor to stimulate nationwide interest in the center and assist in its programs.

THE JOSEPH H. HIRSHHORN MUSEUM AND SCULPTURE GARDEN

Planned for the Mall near Seventh Street and Independence Avenue, S.W., the Joseph H. Hirshhorn Museum and Sculpture Garden will house what has been regarded as the largest and most important art collection in private hands. By virtue of Joseph Hirshhorn's munificence, it left private hands for public custody on November 7, 1966, when Congress accepted Hirshhorn's gift, authorized a site for the construction of the building, and provided statutory authority for the appropriation of construction and operating funds. In his message to Congress requesting the enabling legislation, President Johnson recalled the great tradition of private contributions that have enriched the cultural life of Washington: Smithson's original bequest that founded the Smithsonian Institution in 1846; William Corcoran's founding of the Corcoran Gallery of Art in 1859; and Charles Freer's and Andrew Mellon's gifts to the nation. It was quite logical that Hirshhorn also sought the aegis of the Smithsonian when he came to decide where his collection, "the fruit of a lifetime of dedicated effort and discerning judgment," as the President described it, should finally repose. Actual construction of the museum and sculpture garden was scheduled to begin before the end of 1970.

The gift included nearly 5,000 paintings and drawings and over 1,500 pieces of sculpture, which have been conservatively valued at $25 million. Hirshhorn also gave $1 million for future acquisitions.

"The Hirshhorn Collection," reported the Smithsonian's house organ *The Torch,*

> is committed to major developments in painting and sculpture. The scope of the sculpture section is international, ranging from antiquity through Benin bronzes of the 16th to 19th centuries to the work of today's young creators. A focal point is its outstanding monumental sculptures, both European and American, from the 19th and 20th centuries. More than 100 of these, including such world-renowned sculptures as Rodin's "The Burghers of Calais," Matisse's four bas-reliefs "The Backs," and Moore's "King and Queen" will be on view in the museum's open court and along the broad walks bordering the reflecting pool of the sculpture garden.
>
> The painting collection focuses on the current century. From the works of precursors such as Thomas Eakins and Winslow Homer to the canvases of the 1960's, the course of painting in America is covered in depth. Complementing the United States section is a strong selection of paintings by modern European masters of the past three decades.
>
> Because of the size and range of its collections, the Hirshhorn Museum will permit the study and exhibition of many major artists in a depth rarely possible. Eakins, Gorky, De Kooning, Matisse, Moore, Miro, and Giacometti are among the outstanding artists represented.

Abram Lerner, curator of the collection since 1955, was named director of the new museum and gallery in 1968. He has said that, upon its completion, the collection will offer the public alternating exhibitions of its permanent collection, a varied schedule of educational programs, and a series of rotating exhibitions.

HILLWOOD: A MUSEUM OF THE FUTURE

A Smithsonian museum of the future lies in Hillwood, a 25-acre estate in northwest Washington, which in January,

1969, was deeded to the stewardship of the Smithsonian by its owner, Mrs. Marjorie Merriweather Post, subject to a life estate. Under the terms of the title transfer, the estate will become a public art museum; included also is a monetary bequest to provide for all expenses of the Hillwood museum and gardens.

The Hillwood mansion, a red-brick Georgian structure, houses the finest collection of Imperial Russian art of the eighteenth and nineteenth centuries to be found anywhere outside the Soviet Union. A full room is dedicated to Russian porcelain, and another houses a unique collection of chalices. Other treasures include creations by Fabergé, jeweler to the Czars; Sèvres porcelain; Beauvaise tapestries; portraits of French and Russian nobility; and eighteenth-century French furniture. Items from the collection are occasionally made available for special exhibitions, and Hillwood itself has frequently been opened to students and scholars.

THE COOPER-HEWITT MUSEUM OF DESIGN

The Cooper Union in New York City was founded in 1859 by the industrialist Peter Cooper as a gesture for social betterment. Its initial objective was to provide free instruction in the arts and sciences and free reading rooms for members of the working class. It was the first school in the United States to offer free courses in adult education and became a popular, going concern, with lecture courses and night schools in engineering, art, technical sciences, stenography and typing, telegraphy, oratory and debate, and other practical subjects. Later, its scope was expanded to include the humanities. It attracted gifts from members of the Cooper family, including Abram S. Hewitt, Peter Cooper's son-in-law, and from such philanthropists as Andrew Carnegie, and accumulated productive funds of several million dollars. By the mid-1960's, the school had an average of 1,300 students in its professional departments and about 1,600 in the adult-education classes. Its library today numbers about 100,000 volumes.

In 1897, three of Peter Cooper's granddaughters, Sarah, Eleanor, and Amy Hewitt, founded the Cooper Union Museum for the Arts of Decoration as an adjunct to the parent organization, and in the following seven decades a large and important collection of art objects accumulated for display and study. By 1963, however, the trustees of Cooper Union began to feel that the museum was extraneous to their primary responsibility of conducting a formal educational program and so proposed its discontinuance. New Yorkers objected, and a committee to save the museum formed; a tidy sum and considerable sentiment were raised, and on the recommendation of the American Association of Museums, the Smithsonian Institution agreed to assume responsibility for the museum's continuance in New York. On October 9, 1967, an agreement was signed giving the museum's entire collection and its related library to the Smithsonian. The following April, the New York State Supreme Court gave its approval to the transaction. The name was changed to the Cooper-Hewitt Museum of Design to honor both Peter Cooper and the three Hewitt sisters. In 1971, the museum is scheduled to move from its present location on the fourth floor of Cooper Union's Foundation Building at Astor Place to the Andrew Carnegie mansion on Fifth Avenue at 91st Street, in an area which has become in the past decade, the city's "Museum Row."

The museum today comprises more than 85,000 objects devoted exclusively to the decorative arts: textiles, embroideries and laces, wallpapers (the greatest collection of old and new wallpapers in the United States), drawings and prints, porcelain and glass, furniture, metalwork, and costume accessories, with emphasis on design rather than on the artist. The collection of drawings contains works, mostly by Italian and French artists, dating from the fifteenth to the nineteenth century. The American drawings, about 8,000 in all, include more than 300 items by Winslow Homer, together with 22 of his oils, and nearly 2,000 by the Hudson River artist Frederic E. Church. The museum's library has 15,000 volumes, 2,000 rare books, and innumerable photographs and clippings.

In 1968, Dr. Richard P. Wunder, a former curator of drawings and prints at the Cooper Union Museum and, since 1964, curator of painting and sculpture of the National Collection of Fine Arts, was named first director of the Cooper-Hewitt Museum of Design—the newest member of what is becoming a prolific Smithsonian family. The museum will be administered under the general direction of the National Collection of Fine Arts. The museum's first exhibiton under the Smithsonian opened in December, 1968, with a display of recent acquisitions, including French eighteenth-century porcelains and contemporary African objects.

It should perhaps be remarked that Washington, D.C., can no longer contain the Smithsonian, as Smithson naïvely thought it might. The words on the old Smithsonian seal—*per orbem*—were indeed prophetic, not only as applied to the global proliferation of Smithsonian influence but also to the Institution's physical habitation.

VIII

Publications, Information, and the Performing Arts

Smithson's will contained a double-barreled charge—the increase and the diffusion of knowledge—and there is no indication that either was meant to be subordinate to the other. These have been the twin jobs of the Institution, and they go hand in hand.

To diffuse knowledge, Joseph Henry thought mainly of publications and, for a short time, of lectures. "It is chiefly by the publications of the Institution," he said, "that its fame is to be spread through the world, and the monument most befitting the name of Smithson erected to his memory." Since Henry's day, other media for dispensing information to the public have been developed, and these have been opportunely used by the Institution. Nevertheless, publication, in one form or another, is still the mainstay, and the publication program, combined with the Institution's other informational and extension activities, has, as Joseph Henry prophesied, spread the Smithsonian's fame throughout the world.

THE INTERNATIONAL EXCHANGE SERVICE

The art of communicating scientific intelligence in Henry's day left much to be desired, and Henry saw the need for a speedy, world-wide exchange of information and the opportunity it offered for the Smithsonian to make a unique contribution. "The worth and importance of the Institution," he declared, "are not to be estimated by what it accumulates within the walls of its building, but by what it sends forth to the world." He wanted the Smithsonian to avoid parochialism and to make an impact abroad. Only three years after the Institution began, he started a program that in time would achieve his aims.

With the appearance in 1848 of its first publication, the Smithsonian faced the problem of how best to distribute copies where they would be useful and accessible. In addition to U.S. distribution, a few hundred copies were sent to scientific and other learned institutions abroad, with the request that these groups exchange publications with the Smithsonian. At first, the number of responses to the proposal was small, but by 1852 Henry reported that 4,744 articles had been received. To continue this desirable exchange, Henry appointed agents in a number of foreign countries. The Royal Society of London was especially cooperative. Gradually, the exchange system expanded until Henry was able to offer to other learned societies of the United States the facilities set up at the Institution for distributing their publications abroad.

As it grew, the exchange service became a clearinghouse for the receipt and distribution of scientific literature. Incoming packages of exchange publications were admitted free of duty and were allowed to pass customs without the delay of an examination. Many of the great transportation companies and steamship lines extended the privilege of free freight to the service.

From the beginning, U.S. Government departments used the service to obtain publications of other governments in exchange for their own. In 1867, Congress passed an act systematizing this government interchange, but it was not until 1881 that congressional financial support was provided. By that time, the exchange service was costing the Institution

so much, in spite of generous free freight and other con-
cessions, that something had to be done, and Congress
assumed part of the program's support by appropriating
$3,000. This support has been continued and increased, and
in 1968, the anual appropriation for the service reached
approximately $130,000.

For about forty years, the international exchanges operated
unofficially, so to speak, from the standpoint of international
law. Beginning in 1875 at international conferences held in
Paris and Brussels, delegates discussed the exchange between
countries not only of government documents but also of
scientific and literary publications, and in 1886 a formal
agreement was reached. Eight nations ratified the convention,
"International Exchange of Official Documents, Scientific
and Literary Publications," and it was officially proclaimed
by President Grover Cleveland on January 15, 1889. Other
nations accepted the convention later, and special arrangements were made for exchanges with countries that had not
ratified the agreement. The Smithsonian Institution was recognized as the official exchange agency of the United States.

The service in operation today functions with slight modification from the system inaugurated by Henry. Libraries,
scientific societies, educational institutions, and individuals in
this country who wish to distribute their publications abroad
as gifts or exchanges send the separately addressed packages
to the Smithsonian, carriage cost prepaid. There, the packages are sorted by country and forwarded with similar shipments from other organizations to one of the thirty-seven
exchange bureaus in other parts of the world, where they are
distributed to the addressees. Similarly, shipments of addressed
packages of publications from the foreign exchange bureaus
are received and distributed free to addressees in the United
States.

The volume of this exchange business is considerable. During the year 1967–68, 1,239,869 packages of publications

weighing 844,413 pounds were received from more than 350 colleges, universities, learned societies, and other organizations in the United States, plus U.S. Government agencies, for transmission to some 100 countries. In return, 68,916 packages of publications weighing 105,861 pounds were received by the service for distribution in the United States. Packages of publications were accepted for transmission to all countries except the mainland of China, North Korea, and North Vietnam.

The only interruptions of the service were those occasioned by the two world wars, when many international communications broke down. Yet even through these years, exchanges were continued with all countries of the Western Hemisphere and with a few elsewhere. The benefits derived from the program are obvious; it is one of small cost but of immeasurable use.

PUBLICATIONS

In most government agencies, publication is a subsidiary or regulatory function. Not so with the Smithsonian Institution, for it is committed to a publishing program to fulfill its mandate. One might say it must publish or perish.

When I first joined the Smithsonian nearly forty years ago, there stood in the great hall of the Institution a 23-foot column of books, rising foursquare nearly to the ceiling, with a label telling the visitor that this column contained no duplicates and that each volume comprised either one or many publications of the Smithsonian, which had been distributed free to fifteen hundred libraries and scientific societies in all countries of the world. This achievement impressed me as diffusion in the optimum sense. The program's impact was well described in a Smithsonian brochure issued in 1964:

> The Smithsonian's publications constitute probably the most widely known phase of the Institution's activities, and it is

certain that great impetus has been given to scientific progress in this country through their use by scientists, research workers, teachers, students, and all others engaged in the increase and promotion of knowledge.

In all, about 12 million copies and parts have been distributed to institutions and private individuals.

Since its founding, the Smithsonian has published close to 15,000 individual books and pamphlets. Until recent years, there was little attempt to popularize the publications. They were printed in small editions, seldom larger than 3,000 copies; they were for the most part on the technical side; and their format was plain and dignified. Often they were books of great scientific importance but ones that commercial publishers could not profitably undertake. By and large, the criterion for publication has been: Is the material a contribution to knowledge, and does it help to fulfill the mission of the Institution, which, as Henry saw it, was "to facilitate the use of all the implements of research and to diffuse the knowledge this use may develop"? It has been this substantial kind of publishing that has spread the Smithsonian's reputation around the globe.

Henry's annual reports were a notable and unique contribution to the publication program. They contained not only an administrative record of the Smithsonian's yearly events and accomplishments but also a general appendix containing a careful selection of twenty to twenty-five articles, presented in language that could be understood by the educated layman, on the progress and the important developments that had taken place in all branches of science and the arts. These reports were government documents, freely and widely distributed. Bound in green cloth (in the earlier days it was brown) and with the Smithsonian torch emblazoned on the spine, they became standard fodder for libraries, teachers, students, and the general public. They ran, without a break, for 115 years, more or less in the pattern that Joseph Henry had started. In 1964, when the reports in that form were discontinued, a great publishing tradition came to an end. The Smithsonian annual report for 1965 contained an explanation of the change: "The objectives of the General Appendix will be met by an annual volume in the nature of a Smithsonian year-book, an anthology of distinguished and important contributions to the sciences and the arts written by authorities in their fields and presented for the general reader." But this promise has not been fully kept, for at present only two of the yearbooks have appeared—*Knowledge Among Men,* eleven essays on science, culture, and society commemorating the two-hundredth anniversary of the birth of James Smithson, published in 1966, and *The Fitness of Man's Environment,* a series of papers delivered at a Smithsonian symposium in February, 1967, and published a year later. These later volumes, however, do not meet the same objectives or reach the same audience of the general public that the former series did.

The entire series of general appendix reports included some three thousand articles, many of them written by request by eminent scientists, others reprinted from scientific journals, particularly those of small circulation. Dr. William Goetzmann, University of Texas historian, praised the series as "a matchless panorama of the nation's scientific past and an indispensable resource for anyone interested in the history of science and culture in the [United States]." Their content was described in *Publishers' Weekly* of March 4, 1968, when a reissue of the reports—many of which had been long out of print—was announced by a private publisher:

In total the reprint series includes approximately 2,000 articles containing personal accounts of their experiments by Marconi, Madame Curie, the Wright Brothers; state-of-the-art surveys in almost all scientific disciplines at various points of time; re-

ports on world-wide scientific surveys and collecting expeditions; philosophical interpretations of the impact of science on
society; evaluations of the works of famous scientists and a
wide variety of long-neglected source materials ranging from
a 1900 eyewitness report on the "Loot of the Imperial Summer
Palace at Pekin" to an 1897 article by Havelock Ellis on
"Mescal, A New Artificial Paradise."

Another series that attained deserving eminence among
scholars was the Smithsonian Contributions to Knowledge,
begun soon after the founding of the Institution. It was quarto
in size and was unique for the times in publishing ample illustration accompanying the monographs, a practice that other
scholarly publishers could not afford to copy. The first of
this series was the now famous work of E. G. Squier and
E. H. Davis, *Ancient Monuments of the Mississippi Valley.* By
1916, when the series was discontinued for reasons of economy, thirty-five volumes had been published, including such
classic works as Samuel P. Langley and Charles M. Manly's
Memoir on Mechanical Flight, Nathaniel S. Shaler's *Comparison of Earth and Moon,* James H. Coffin's *The Winds of
the Globe,* Edward W. Morley's *On the Densities of Oxygen
and Hydrogen, and the Ratio of Their Atomic Weights,* and
Lewis Henry Morgan's *Systems of Consanguinity and Affinity
of the Human Family.*

The objectives of the Contributions were assumed in large
part by the Smithsonian Miscellaneous Collections, similar
in content but octavo in size. Over 150 volumes of the Collections have been issued, containing many major contributions
in chemistry, physics, anthropology, biology, geology, bibliography, and almost any other science that can be named. The
Collections have also included a series of tables—Physical
Tables, Meteorological Tables, Geographical Tables, Logarith-
mic Tables, Tables of Hyperbolic Functions—that have long
been standard works of reference.

As the years passed, many other publication series were

instituted. Some dropped by the wayside; others continued; but, at one time or another, most of the Smithsonian bureaus were accommodated with their own special series. A complete list, as of 1969, demonstrates in a general way the size and scope of the publication program:

1. Annual reports of the Board of Regents to Congress (currently entitled *The Smithsonian Year*)
2. Smithsonian Contributions to Knowledge (terminated in 1916)
3. Smithsonian Miscellaneous Collections (terminated in 1969)
4. Annual reports of the U.S. National Museum
5. Bulletins of the U.S. National Museum
6. Contributions from the Museum of History and Technology (subseries of the Bulletins of the U.S. National Museum; terminated in 1969)
7. Contributions from the U.S. National Herbarium (subseries of the Bulletins of the U.S. National Museum; terminated in 1969)
8. Proceedings of the U.S. National Museum (terminated in 1969)
9. Annual reports of the Bureau of American Ethnology (terminated with the demise of the bureau in 1964)
10. Bulletins of the Bureau of American Ethnology (terminated in 1966)
11. Publications of the Institute of Social Anthropology (none issued after 1953)
12. Smithsonian Contributions to Anthropology
13. Smithsonian Contributions to Botany
14. Smithsonian Contributions to the Earth Sciences
15. Smithsonian Contributions to Paleobiology
16. Smithsonian Contributions to Zoology
17. Smithsonian Studies in History and Technology
18. Smithsonian Contributions to Astrophysics
19. Smithsonian Annals of Flight

20. Annals of the Astrophysical Observatory
21. Catalogues of the National Collection of Fine Arts
22. Oriental Studies of the Freer Gallery of Art
23. Freer Gallery of Art Occasional Papers
24. Ars Orientalis (published jointly with the University of Michigan)
25. Catalogues of the National Gallery of Art
26. Smithsonian special publications, of many sizes and varieties, some of a popular nature

In addition, information leaflets, folders, color slides, guide books, postcards, film strips, and other popular items are distributed in large numbers.

The distribution of Smithsonian publications has its complex side. Those printed from government funds are in general considered as government documents and are released through the Government Printing Office. Those issued from Smithsonian funds are nongovernmental and are controlled and distributed by the Institution, some free to libraries and co-operators but most by sale.

From time to time, the Institution has undertaken special publication projects. In 1925, for example, it published a set of five portfolios containing over four hundred plates of water-color sketches of wildflowers by Mary Vaux Walcott, wife of Secretary Walcott. These beautiful deluxe volumes, now out of print, employed the best techniques of color printing then available and became collectors' items for bibliophiles, botanists, and wildflower enthusiasts. A part of the proceeds from the sale of these plates was set aside in a special fund to underwrite the production of other Smithsonian publications in botany. During World War II, a special series called War Background Studies was produced. Twenty-one in number, they comprised illustrated booklets on the peoples, history, geography, natural history, and other features of areas that the war reached, especially in the Pacific. At the end of the war, more than 630,000 copies had been printed, including 400,000 especially for the armed services.

A staff of editors and their assistants comprised the Editorial and Publications Division, under which the publications activities of the Institution were long organized. Just prior to the retirement of the chief of that division in 1966, the unit began to be called the Smithsonian Institution Press, and certain responsibilities that the division had long shouldered were reorganized into separate units, such as press and public-relations activities, radio and television promotion, lecture and function arrangements. When the new director, Anders Richter, from the University of Chicago Press, took over in the spring of 1966, the name Smithsonian Institution Press became official, and much of the work increasingly assumed a university-press image. The Institution has been a member of the Association of American University Presses since 1960, a recognition of the long-standing scholarly nature of Smithsonian publications. In fact, no member press of the Association has been publishing in the United States longer than the Smithsonian.

Another new development is the abandonment of several old publication series for new ones determined along subject-matter lines. This trend started with the initiation of Smithsonian Contributions to Astrophysics, Contributions from the Museum of History and Technology, Smithsonian Annals of Flight, and Smithsonian Contributions to Anthropology. New series have been inaugurated for other scientific disciplines such as zoology, the earth sciences, and paleobiology.

In recent years, the Smithsonian has engaged in an increasing number of cooperative publication ventures with such institutions as the American Association of Museums and with commercial publishers. This program actually started with a series of twelve volumes published in several editions and revisions beginning in 1925. A series of popular books on science, written by members or associates of the

Smithsonian staff, was published by The Series Publishers, an ad hoc firm, with royalties paid to the Institution. Secretary Abbot assumed general editorship of the series, known as the Smithsonian Scientific Series, and wrote two of the volumes— *The Sun and the Welfare of Man* and *Great Inventions.* These twelve books proved extremely successful, and the Institution realized in the neighborhood of $500,000 from royalties.

In 1960, a 3-volume set, *Smithsonian Treasury of Science,* comprised of contributions that had appeared in the appendixes of the annual reports and edited by former Smithsonian publications chief W. P. True, was published in cooperation with Simon & Schuster of New York, followed in 1966 by the *Smithsonian Treasury of 20th-Century Science,* a 1-volume anthology of annual report articles. From the same source, Bessie Z. Jones in 1966 compiled *The Golden Treasury of Science,* "30 portraits of Giants of 19th-Century Science by Their Scientific Contemporaries." *Knowledge Among Men,* the first of the Smithsonian Annuals, was published in the same year. Cooperative publishing contracts have also been negotiated with other publishers, one of whom acts as distributing agent for certain Smithsonian publications.

Obviously, it is impossible here to mention more than a few of the thousands of Smithsonian publications. Some have been cited throughout this book, and a very selected list is given in Appendix B.

THE LIBRARY

The Smithsonian Library dates from the Institution's founding; the original act made specific provisions for a library, and Charles Coffin Jewett was appointed librarian early in 1847. The library's initial objective was to procure "a complete collection of the memoirs and transactions of learned societies throughout the world and an entire series of the most important and literary periodicals," and it succeeded to a large extent in accomplishing this task. In six years, the collection, largely by exchange, grew to 32,000 volumes. Henry felt strongly that, although a modest library of scientific literature was needed for the use of its own staff, it was not the function of the Institution to build up a large national library in competition with the Library of Congress and other institutions. He believed the Smithsonian Library should work in cooperation with other libraries but avoid needless duplication.

One example of such duplication was the matter of copyright. For nearly thirteen years after the founding of the Institution, the law required anyone wishing to secure copyright of a book to deposit one copy with the librarian of the Smithsonian Institution and another copy with the librarian of Congress. This dual requirement, it seemed to Henry, was unnecessary and promised to become burdensome, and in 1857 he succeeded in having section 10 of the original Act of 1846 repealed. The Library of Congress thereafter became the sole copyright depository.

A few years later, in 1866, another merger was effected. The Smithsonian Library, by congressional authority, turned over to the Library of Congress about 40,000 volumes of scientific works to form the basis of what became known as the Smithsonian Deposit. "The object of this transfer," wrote Henry, "is not to separate this unique and highly prized collection of books from its relations to the Smithsonian Institution, for it must still bear its name and be subject to its control, but merely to deposit it where its preservation will be more certain [thinking possibly of the fire in the Smithsonian Building] and its usefulness more extended." In the years that have passed since the original deposit, at least 1 million volumes and parts have been added to it, making it one of the largest collections of scientific literature in the world. It is especially complete in the transactions and proceedings of scientific societies. The collection is no longer maintained as a deposit separate from other Library of Congress holdings.

Today the main body of the library is housed in the Natural History Building. It is no longer officially referred to as the Smithsonian Library, but as the Smithsonian Institution Libraries, inasmuch as it comprises also several good-sized branch libraries attached to various Smithsonian bureaus and departments. For example, the library from the old Bureau of American Ethnology, now included in the Department of Anthropology, contains one of the finest collections of ethnological material anywhere. The National Herbarium has an extensive botanical library, as do, in their respective fields, the Department of Entomology, the Radiation Biology Laboratory, the National Museum of History and Technology, the Smithsonian Astrophysical Observatory, and the various art galleries.

The Smithsonian libraries not only serve the staff of the Institution in their scholarly endeavors but also constitute a rich body of source material for use by the entire Washington community and beyond. In addition to more than 1 million books—a total that exceeds that of any university library in the Washington area—the collections include documents, manuscripts, films, photographs, and the like.

All in all, the Smithsonian libraries are operated as working collections to support the Institution's various research programs and museum activities. They are primarily scientific, specializing in geology, botany, zoology, anthropology, aeronautics, astrophysics, and systematics, but also with sizable holdings in American history and technology, art, museology, early works of travel and exploration, philately, history of American industry and technology, and general trade literature. The Smithsonian takes pride in their utility rather than in any incunabular or esoteric holdings, although the collections are not without rarities.

PUBLIC AFFAIRS

The Smithsonian's Office of Public Affairs is a relatively new organization, though the various activities for which it is responsible—public information, press relations, radio and television liaison, audiovisual services, community relations, and special events—have been going on for a long time. The office was created in 1967 to succeed the so-called Office of Information, which in turn evolved from a portion of the Editorial and Publications Division, which for many years had handled all the Institution's public information activities.

Over most of its history, the public relations of the Institution were promoted in a low key and almost entirely under its private funds, the philosophy being that the multifarious work of the Institution would largely speak for itself. This soft approach did very well for a long time, but public-relations techniques have grown, and the Institution began hankering for the greater attention it deserves. I remember some years ago attending a congressional appropriations committee hearing at which the Smithsonian budget was being justified. At a point when certain of the arguments seemed to be rather unconvincing in the face of some searching though caustic comments from the committee, a congressman remarked, "What you ought to have down there is a good public-relations program." Yet no one present doubted that the gentleman would have been the last one to vote for funds for such a purpose. Public funds for public relations have never come easily.

The Smithsonian has always endeavored to keep the public informed about its work, to answer its questions, and to offer education in science and the arts. New ways of performing these functions have been adopted as communication techniques have changed.

The Institution began issuing press releases about 1917

and has been doing so for half a century. To a large extent, these releases have been based on the Institution's research, explorations, and publications, as well as on the more newsworthy of Smithsonian activities and events. For a long time, in fact, they constituted a sort of popular science service and were widely used by newspapers, magazines, press services, and special writers throughout the country. Most of them, of course, did not contain hot news, but they provided the press with reliable information for a science-hungry public. Other institutions in Washington, such as Science Service and the National Geographic Society, were doing a similar job, but there was room for all, and the type of release that the Smithsonian issued was unique in style and content and filled, as one man said, "a very vacant void."

The Institution entered the radio field in 1923, when it sponsored a series of weekly science talks over a local Washington station. The program lasted for over four years and was among the very first series of science talks to be given via the medium. Ten years later, in cooperation with the National Broadcasting Company and the U.S. Office of Education, and with the professional help of WPA actors and writers, the unsponsored Smithsonian radio show "The World Is Yours" was inaugurated. It was a half-hour dramatization of a variety of topics in science, history, technology, and the arts and was broadcast over about eighty-five stations every week for six years. It was terminated only when the exigencies of World War II pre-empted air time. After the war, it was impossible to reassemble the support, talent, and conditions that made this show so successful and popular, and it was not returned to the air. During its lifetime, though, it had drawn attention to the Smithsonian in a way that has not been equaled since.

With the advent of television, the Smithsonian attempted sporadically to interest the networks in a nationwide series of television broadcasts based on the almost unlimited Smithsonian material available, but such a program did not materialize, principally because Smithsonian officials balked at the idea of the Institution, as a quasi-governmental agency, being regularly, commercially sponsored. During this period, Smithsonian television activity was confined to cooperating with commercial stations in the production of one-shot broadcasts based on Smithsonian material.

In the mid-1950's, a widely representative group of educational and cultural institutions in the Washington, D.C., area began to take steps toward the organization of an educational television station, following the assignment by the Federal Communications Commission of ultra-high-frequency channels to noncommercial television (now usually referred to as ETV). The Greater Washington Educational Television Association was organized and immediately began a program to obtain financial support and to educate the Washington-area public about ETV. Their progress was slow and often discouraging, but finally, in October, 1961, the Association's own station, WETA, went on the air. From the start, the Smithsonian was a member of the corporation and was (and still is) represented on its board of trustees. Although the Institution had no funds to devote to ETV at that time, it helped establish the now-flourishing project and has continued its assistance by furnishing occasional program material.

In 1967, the Institution went on the air with a weekly half-hour filmed color series entitled "The Smithsonian." Produced by NBC, it was addressed to such subjects as underwater archeology, aviation and space flights, election campaigns, ecology, conservation, George Catlin and the American Indian, systematics, and American folk art. It reached an estimated 4 million viewers. In 1968, two television shows were produced: "The Enormous Egg," a children's story of a pet dinosaur; and a documentary on the ecology of East Africa. All in all, Smithsonian television activities are looking up.

The Office of Public Affairs also performs a number of other services for the Smithsonian and for the general public. It prepares and oversees publication of the Institution's house organs; it conducts the Smithsonian's Free Film Theater, which presents educational films of broad interest; it operates an audio-visual library and distributes educational motion pictures, slides, and still photographs throughout the country; and it engineers two recorded telephone information services for the Washington, D.C., area: Dial-A-Museum, which provides up-to-the-minute information on the day's events and highlights of new museum exhibits; and Dial-A-Satellite, which presents information on artificial satellites and other visible celestial objects.

DIVISION OF PERFORMING ARTS

The Division of Performing Arts was created on July 1, 1967, to manage and produce programs for the education and aesthetic enjoyment of the museum visitor. "The 'lively arts,' " said the division's director James Morris, "are vitally important as means of cultural transmission," and the new division, drawing its staff from members of the former Museum Services Division, has set about providing the vehicles for such transmission. During its first year, the division arranged twenty-six Smithsonian productions, which were attended by a total of 604,500 persons. The events included a 4-day Festival of American Folklife on Washington's Mall; several concerts featuring such entertainment as chamber music and barbershop quartets; two weeks of puppet theater; and a performance by a dance company. A *son et lumière* production, featuring the re-creation of history by means of sounds, voices, and highly developed lighting techniques, has been under consideration recently. The division also promotes an annual Rites of Spring festival in Washington, in which city parks and recreation centers are used for such events as balloon flights, music, carousel rides, athletic demonstrations, poster and collage exhibits, and other *al fresco* demonstrations. Congressman Andrew Jacobs of Indiana was so impressed with the 1968 Rites that he remarked in the *Congressional Record*, "The Institution seems to understand that culture is a total way of life of a people, not merely a treasure house for academicians or a plaything for the elite."

SCIENCE INFORMATION EXCHANGE

What is now the Science Information Exchange (SIE) was brought under the Smithsonian wing in 1954. It was first called Bio-Science Information Exchange, but, as its usefulness expanded, its scope was broadened to include the sciences in general. The operation had previously been nurtured by the National Academy of Sciences. Its support derived from a number of federal agencies whose research directors and administrators realized that the management of multi-million-dollar research programs could be facilitated by prompt exchange of information about programs in progress. The enterprise grew so rapidly that support and management problems became complex and burdensome for individual agencies. As a result, in 1964 the National Science Foundation took over the responsibility for funding and over-all management of the program, with operational management left under the aegis of the Smithsonian.

The exchange, housed in an office building in downtown Washington, receives, organizes, and disseminates information on scientific research in progress. Its mission is to assist the planning and management of research activities supported by government and nongovernment agencies and institutions by promoting an exchange of information, prior to publication, on subject matter and other data of current research. The exchange helps program directors and administrators avoid unwarranted duplication and determine the most advantageous distribution of research funds. It serves the entire scientific community by informing individual investigators about who is currently working on problems in their special fields.

Each research record of SIE includes the name of the supporting agency, the names of principal and associate investigators, the location of research work, the level of effort, and the dates of active work. A description of the research in progress is analyzed by staff scientists, indexed, and stored to insure retrieval of all records related to any specific research element or broad topic. Needless to say, the operation is thoroughly computerized.

The use and service of the exchange continue to grow year by year. In his 1968 report, the director, Dr. Monroe E. Freeman, stated that registration with the exchange of current projects from government and nongovernment research totaled more than 97,000 during the year, that over 8,000 questions had been answered for individual scientists, and that over 300,000 copies of individual research summaries had been made available to the national scientific community.

SMITHSONIAN ASSOCIATES

The establishment of the Smithsonian Associates was announced by Secretary Ripley in September, 1965, during the celebration of the two-hundredth anniversary of the birth of James Smithson. This organization, a sort of society of friends of the Institution, is patterned after similar "friends" groups enjoyed by other museums and cultural institutions. Its objective is to encourage support of and participation in the Institution's activities and programs by people throughout the nation and gradually build up a grass-roots community of Smithsonianophiles. By paying nominal annual dues, members express their interest in sharing directly in the work of the Institution in science, art, and history. For their modest contribution, they are entitled to special services—lectures, concerts, film showings, craft shows, programs for children, exhibit openings, guided tours, publications.

By the end of 1968, membership in the Smithsonian Associates stood at 7,000, representing about 15,000 persons, and had, according to the director, "expanded in depth and breadth." Over 2,300 members attended luncheon talks on the arts and the humanities and tea talks on American arts and ideas. A travel program was begun in which 3,500 members participated in walking tours of Washington as well as trips to several museums outside the city. Also included were such camping and field trips as mushroom, rock, and fossil hunts; shore strolls; insect, botany, and geology walks; and industrial and salvage archeology expeditions. Special events included a kite carnival on Washington's Mall, a zoo night, a Potomac cruise, and puppet shows. The programs, now well under way, have succeeded in creating wider popular interest in the Smithsonian's work and have demonstrated the inexhaustible potential of the Institution. The director believes that "a new vitality has been created by this close interplay between the Smithsonian's professional staff and an interested public. The extent of its reach is an exciting speculation."

OFFICE OF INTERNATIONAL ACTIVITIES

It remains to describe some of the other Smithsonian activities that illustrate the growing trend to extend and diffuse the Institution's programs and to re-enforce their total impact outside its immediate walls. One of the most far-reaching of these is that now formalized in the Office of International Activities. Soon after taking office in 1964, Secretary Ripley appointed a consultant for international activities "to explore appropriate areas of international cooperation," the conviction being that a need and an opportunity existed to carry the Smithsonian's activities beyond the Institution's traditional overseas field expeditions and research. The Department of State's Bureau of Educational and Cultural Affairs agreed that the Smithsonian might exercise a leading role in administering overseas archeological projects that were financed by excess foreign currencies available through agricultural surplus sales under P.L. 480.

Under the leadership of a consultant, William W. Warner, the Institution's international activities expanded. Warner then became the first director of the Office of International Activities, in which post he remained until early in 1968, when he was elevated to the Institution's newly created position of acting assistant secretary for Public Service. By that time, the appropriation to the Smithsonian of U.S.-owned P.L. 480 funds abroad had reached the annual total of $2.32 million, furnishing a dependable source of support for the program, which in general maintained a scholarly focus on disciplines of interest to the Smithsonian, notably (but by no means exclusively) anthropology. Expenditures are in the form of research grants. At the end of the third year of operations, more than a hundred such grants had been awarded, benefiting the research programs of more than forty American institutions of higher learning. Members of the research staff of the Institution also share in the overseas projects through grants from the fund to the Smithsonian Research Foundation.

Many of these grants support continuing projects, such as, to name but one, the Carnegie Museum–University of Pittsburgh excavations at Ashdod in Israel, which have confirmed Biblical accounts of this Philistine city's periodic destruction and have unearthed occupation sequences ranging from the late Bronze Age to the Byzantine period. Major programs are also in progress in Egypt, Tunisia, India, Yugoslavia, and Ceylon. Other countries included are Burma, Guinea, Pakistan, Poland, and Morocco.

By nature, the work of the Office of International Affairs is highly cooperative, and its staff must keep in touch with such groups as the Organization of American States, UNESCO, and the Institute of International Education. The work is varied. For example, the office served as coordinator in negotiations between the Department of Defense, the National Academy of Sciences, and the Royal Society in establishing the Indian Ocean island of Aldabra as an international conservation area; worked out an agreement for a long-term ecological research program at the new wildlife refuge at St. Vincent Island, Florida; and cooperated with the Department of Commerce in planning the federal building at the 1968 Hemisfair in San Antonio. Another service is that of coordinating the travel and research of foreign scholars visiting the Smithsonian.

OTHER EXTENSION PROGRAMS

Another very successful extension operation is the Smithsonian Institution Traveling Exhibition Service (SITES), which began in 1952 as an adjunct of the National Collection of Fine Arts. For the most part self-supporting from income received from rental fees paid by galleries and other sponsors of the traveling exhibits, the service rapidly waxed in stature and usefulness and became virtually an autonomous unit. In 1966, its jurisdiction was transferred to the U.S. National Museum. SITES circulates exhibitions of cultural and educational value throughout the United States and Canada as a service to museums, galleries, colleges, libraries, and their public. Though its first exhibitions were generally limited to certain fine arts, it has gradually enlarged its scope to include design and crafts, photography, architecture, history, and science. Its exhibitions are assembled from many sources in this country and abroad—museums, public and private institutions, and collectors, who increasingly appreciate the service as a means of sharing their treasures with a wider public. In May, 1968, its catalogue listed 116 available exhibitions. SITES has published a series of distinguished catalogues of a number of the exhibitions it has sponsored, notable among which have been *7,000 Years of Iranian Art, Tutankhamen Treasures, Art Treasures of Turkey, Dürer and His Time, Drawings from Chatsworth, Indian Miniatures,* and a series on masterpieces of Italian, Dutch, Swiss, and French drawing covering five centuries.

The Smithsonian's museums and art galleries in Washington are all located in the downtown area and draw millions of visitors every year from all over the world. In 1967, Secretary Ripley, in spite of this ever increasing attendance, thought that there must be thousands of people in outlying communities who do not visit museums in downtown centers but who nevertheless are museum-hungry. With the help of grants from a number of private foundations, the Smithsonian started an experimental community museum in a renovated theater in Anacostia in Southeast Washington. The small museum opened on September 15, 1967—the first of its kind in the nation—with six exhibits, all designed for visitor participation: a Mercury space capsule, a walk-through reproduction of an 1890 Anacostia store, a little theater with closed-circuit television, shoebox collections on many natural-science subjects, skeletons that could be disassembled, and a small zoo.

The museum is truly a cooperative project. Programs are coordinated with area schools, and local citizens and businessmen participate in planning exhibits. During its first year of operations, the museum attracted 80,000 visitors. Though school groups and individuals from the entire Washington area visit it, the museum has developed a neighborhood identity.

By its very nature, the museum must expand, but it has not been an easy task to raise money to keep the project going. The director, John Kinard, says that the museum has cost almost twice as much as originally anticipated. Nevertheless, it is hardly likely that so worthwhile an experiment will be allowed to languish, and the idea is certain to spread to other large cities.

DIVISION OF INFORMATION SYSTEMS

The growing complexity of gathering and recording information within the Institution necessitated the establishment in 1966 of the Division of Information Systems. Utilizing modern computer technology, the division operates to assemble and preserve masses of information associated with the Smithsonian's museum collections. It serves as a retainer, interpreter, and diagnostician of information problems within the Institution and, to the extent that its resources permit, provides expertise to the museum community in general.

BELMONT CONFERENCE CENTER

In 1964, with the aid of foundation grants, the Smithsonian acquired Belmont, a 340-acre estate of rolling fields and woodlands bordering the Patapsco River and Park near Elkridge, Maryland, 35 miles northeast of Washington and 12 miles southwest of Baltimore. The Belmont mansion was built in 1738 by Caleb Dorsey of Annapolis. Since 1805, when Priscilla Dorsey married Alexander Hanson, the Belmont estate has passed through several generations of the Dorsey-Hanson families. The Smithsonian has now dedicated it to use as a conference center "to provide a peaceful location in pleasant surroundings for the pursuit and sharing of knowledge," particularly in the fields of the Smithsonian's special interests—the sciences, history, and art. Belmont conferences are organized either entirely under Smithsonian auspices or by outside groups. The center began regular operation in 1967, and during May and June of that year conferences were held there by the American Historical Association, the Smithsonian Society of Associates, the American Academy of Arts and Sciences, the U.S. Office of Education Postdoctoral Fellows, and Outward Bound. By the second year, Belmont had been the setting for forty conferences sponsored by thirty private organizations and federal commissions and agencies.

Belmont is set up as a nonprofit organization operating under the aegis of the Smithsonian as a private educational agency. Its board of advisers represents a wide range of interests, and its council of management is selected from members of the board. The resident director reports to the council. The estate provides comfortable residential quarters for twenty-two guests and lecture and discussion accommodations for fifty. In addition to the main conference room, which seats thirty-six, special rooms for informal meetings are provided.

IX

The Buildings

Early photographs of what is now the Mall in downtown Washington picture a bleak scene indeed. So-called Washington City, with a population of only 61,122 in 1860, was not really a city at all, but, as one commentator described it, a "shabby Southern village scattered over a grandiose plan." Grass grew in the less-used streets, which were muddy and unpaved. There was a slave pen, and domestic animals wandered about. Then, as now, the city was noted for its sweltering summers, when the "sun heated the rough brick sidewalks to the breaking point."

The Smithsonian Building stood out in this setting like a sore thumb. William H. Dall described it in his biography of Spencer Baird:

The Smithsonian building was on the Mall in southwest Washington, known as the 'Island,' because it was separated by the shallow and odiferous James Creek [also called Tiber Creek] from the main part of the town. The Mall had been laid out by A. J. Downing, with fine taste, and was full of shrubbery, grass and trees, but was little cared for, so that in it birds and small beasts found haven. The building was on the south side, facing north. . . . It was approached by paths and driveways sparsely sprinkled with river gravel and ankle deep in mud on rainy days. The Washington Monument to the west was a mere stump, and the Capitol, to the east, far from being the stately

181

building of the present. It was not a pleasant undertaking then to reach the Smithsonian building on slushy winter days.

When I first went to Washington, in 1925, the Smithsonian grounds had lost their miasmal character but still retained their informal, parklike appearance. The trees and shrubs and park benches were still there, and red-headed woodpeckers nested in an old hemlock outside my office window. In the mid-1930's, the Mall was leveled off into a long vista of greensward and straight avenues from the Capitol to the Washington Monument and assumed the streamlined look it has today.

There are seven Smithsonian buildings flanking the Mall between Fifth and Fourteenth streets, and two more have been authorized to be built there. A few blocks to the north, the Old Patent Office Building houses two Smithsonian art galleries, and in 1969 some Smithsonian offices moved to the old Pension Office. In Rock Creek Park, a few minutes by car from the Mall, are the buildings of the National Zoological Park, where a long-range development program is in progress.

These buildings, which house the Institution's multifarious activities and attractions, have not sprung up overnight. Until the 1960's, long intervals divided periods of construction. For a hundred years and more funds were shamefully slow in coming from the federal government for new Smithsonian facilities, and private gifts for buildings were restricted to art galleries and the John F. Kennedy Center for the Performing Arts.

The "Castle"

In the act that established the Smithsonian, Congress placed on the Board of Regents the responsibility for the choice of a site and for the erection of a building to be the home of the Institution. It was to be of "plain and durable materials and structure, without unnecessary ornament, and of sufficient size, and with suitable rooms or halls for the re-

SMITHSONIAN INSTITUTION BUILDINGS IN WASHINGTON, D.C.

1. SMITHSONIAN INSTITUTION BUILDING
2. ARTS AND INDUSTRIES BUILDING
3. AIR AND SPACE BUILDING
4. FREER GALLERY OF ART
5. MUSEUM OF HISTORY AND TECHNOLOGY
6. MUSEUM OF NATURAL HISTORY
7. NATIONAL GALLERY OF ART
8. NATIONAL ZOOLOGICAL PARK
9. FINE ARTS AND PORTRAIT GALLERIES

ception and arrangement, upon a liberal scale, of objects of natural history, including a geological and mineralogical cabinet; also, a chemical laboratory, a library, a gallery of art, and the necessary lecture rooms."

The committee appointed by the board to select an architect reported that, out of thirteen designs submitted to them, they had "unanimously selected two, by Mr. James Renwick, junior, of New York City; one of these designs being in the Decorated Gothic style, the other in the Norman." Renwick had just recently designed New York City's Grace Church, which was ready for dedication in 1846, and the committee was no doubt mightily impressed with "Renwick's toothpick" at the head of Broadway. Regent Robert Dale Owen, a member of the committee, a scholar, and something of a connoisseur of architecture himself, was enthusiastic about Renwick's designs. Before the Smithsonian Building was finished, he had written a book entitled *Hints on Public Architecture* in which both Grace Church and the Smithsonian structure were handsomely depicted. The Smithsonian Building was delineated at great length:

The style of Architecture selected is that of the last half of the twelfth century; the latest variety of the rounded style, as it is found immediately anterior to the merging of that manner in the early Gothic. In his general design and in most of his details, the architect has adhered, with a good deal of strictness, to the forms and characteristic enrichments of the period to which this style is referable. The general feeling, however, which pervades his design, especially in the principal towers, is that of a somewhat later era, when all lingering reminiscences of the Post and Lintel manner had been shaken off, and the ruling principles of Arch Architecture were recognized and carried out. I am not acquainted with any actual example yet remaining from what has been variously called the Lombard, the Norman, the Romanesque and the Byzantine school, with which the Smithsonian building will not favorably compare. In so far as the architect has permitted himself to innovate upon ancient precedents from the style in which he designed, he has done so, in my judgment, with discretion and advantage.

"It will be," he continued," the first edifice in the style of the twelfth century and of a character not ecclesiastical, ever erected in this country." In his conclusion, Owen allowed himself perhaps not a little fulsomeness in his praise for Renwick's design. He was certainly no prophet:

> I esteem myself fortunate . . . in being able to refer to an actual example, at our Seat of Government, the architect of which seems to me to have struck into the right road, to have made a step in advance, and to have given us, in his design, not a little of what may be fitting and appropriate in any manner (should the genius of our country hereafter work such out), that shall deserve to be named as a National Style of Architecture for America.

On May 1, 1847, with impressive ceremonies, the cornerstone of the Smithsonian Building was laid. A public holiday was declared, and six or seven thousand persons turned out for the occasion. A mile-long procession, including the District of Columbia militia, several Masonic delegations, and three military bands, moved along F Street to the White House and then proceeded, via Pennsylvania Avenue and Twelfth Street, to the south side of the site, where a platform had been erected and where President Polk, who had personally helped select the site for the building, his Cabinet, and other dignitaries were received in line. The building's cornerstone was laid by Benjamin B. French, Masonic grand master of the District of Columbia, who held the gavel used by President George Washington in laying the cornerstone of the U.S. Capitol and wore the Masonic apron presented to Washington by the Grand Lodge of France through General Lafayette. Grand Chaplain J. N. McJilton, of the Grand Lodge of

Maryland, offered a prayer; Vice-President George Mifflin Dallas, Chancellor of the Smithsonian Board of Regents, delivered an address; and the Reverend French S. Evans pronounced the benediction. With all these fine details on record, it is rather too bad that no one thought to say just where the cornerstone was laid. Though we know what it contains— gold and silver U.S. coins, a report of the Committee on Organization, the Constitution of the United States, the New Testament, the Declaration of Independence, the *Congressional Directory* for 1847, bulletins of the National Institute, a report of the first National Fair at Washington, a report of the U.S. agent appointed to receive the legacy of James Smithson, a medallion portrait of James Smithson, reports of the commissioner of patents, the journal of the proceedings of the Board of Regents for 1846, and a plate with an engraved inscription—the exact location of this illustrious deposit is today unknown.

The completion of the building was attended by a series of headaches, which Henry took pains to elaborate in his annual reports. At first, he tried to rationalize the situation by saying that

> the delay has not only been attended with advantage in husbanding the funds, but also in allowing a more complete adaptation of the interior to the purposes of the Institution. It is surely better, in the construction of such an edifice, to imitate the example of the mollusk, who, in fashioning his shell, adapts it to the form and dimensions of his body, rather than that of another animal who forces himself into a house intended for a different occupant.

But the work dragged on.

By April, 1849, the east wing was completed to the point that the Secretary and his family and staff could move in. Before the end of that year, the west wing was finished and opened for public lectures.

In 1852, Renwick's contract expired and a U.S. Army engineer took over. In 1857, the building committee thought it was through with its job, though a large portion of the interior was still unfinished and was to remain so for several years. Then, on January 24, 1865, a fire destroyed the roof, all the insides of the upper story of the main part of the building, and the interior of the two large north towers and the large south tower. A new architect, Adolph Cluss, was employed, not only to plan and superintend the reconstruction but also to remedy defective parts of the structure. In the major reconstruction that followed, the lecture hall and art gallery were replaced by an exhibit hall that housed, for a time, the U.S. National Museum. By the summer of 1867, the building was again ready for occupancy, but today there still seems to be as much uncertainty as to the date of its actual completion as there is to the location of the cornerstone.

By this time, Secretary Henry was no longer illusioned. On June 28, 1870, he was invited to appear before the English Government Scientific Commission meeting at Westminster. When asked the question "What does the building itself represent?" he replied:

Externally a Norman castle, and it has cost a very large sum. Unfortunately, architecture is frequently in antagonism with science, and, too often, when an architect gets his hand into the purse of an establishment, everything else must stand aside. Much trouble has resulted from this building; it has been a source of constant anxiety and expense, the cost having greatly exceeded the original estimate.

When finally completed, the building had cost nearly $250,000.

The Smithsonian Building is now about 115 years old and has become a symbol of science and learning, as familiar to most Americans as the U.S. Capitol, the Statue of Liberty, and Independence Hall. It is perhaps more an architectural curiosity than a paragon, reminiscent, according to an old guidebook, of "the palace of the old Scotch kings, Holyrood."

The stone for the building, a reddish-brown freestone, was quarried from the banks of the Chesapeake and Ohio Canal near Seneca, Maryland, within twenty-five miles of the building's site. The length of the structure from east to west measures 447 feet, and its greatest width is 160 feet. Its nine towers of various shapes range from 60 to 145 feet in height. The Smithsonian grounds, extending from Seventh to Twelfth streets, N.W., were laid out by Andrew Jackson Downing, a landscape gardener of considerable reputation who also designed the grounds for the Capitol and the White House.

In the beginning, the Smithsonian Building housed not only all the Institution's activities—the museum, the library, the art gallery, the laboratories, the lecture room, the offices—but also some members of the staff, who had rooms in the towers, and Secretary and Mrs. Henry and their four children, who lived in the east wing. Indeed, the family's residence in the building spanned the entire period of the Civil War and lasted until Henry's death in 1878. Their home was a bright spot, a center of Washington intellectual life, with visiting scientists, professors, writers, lecturers, and officers always welcome.

Today, the building is used almost entirely for the top administrative offices of the Institution. In the Great Hall, open to the public, are exhibits that summarize the various activities of the Smithsonian, and from the north foyer may be viewed the tomb of James Smithson. Extensively remodeled in recent years for more efficient office use, the building has lost most of the genteel shabbiness for which it was long famous. There are plans for preserving and further renovating Renwick's "castle on the Mall" so that, according to Secretary Ripley, "the spirit of Renwick's design for this building will be preserved, but redesigned for amenities in such a way that it will stand as a visible symbol of the paramount intellectual position and stature of the Institution it houses." This project, whose cost will be many times that of the original building, is now under way.

THE "ANNEX": TODAY'S ARTS AND INDUSTRIES BUILDING

The collections and exhibits of the National Museum grew apace, and the need for more space came to a head in 1876. In November of that year, the great Centennial Exposition in Philadelphia closed, and the Smithsonian, partly through assistant secretary Baird's opportune solicitation, became the recipient of a real museum bonanza—the many federal and state exhibits, as well as those of several foreign countries, that had been shown at this world's fair celebrating the hundredth year of American independence. Of the foreign exhibits, Henry reported that "the best and most important were presented to the United States at the close of the exhibition, embracing many complete series of objects, illustrating the geology, metallurgy, and ethnology, and the general resources of the nations. Of about 40 governments and colonies, the choicest of the exhibits of the 34 were presented to the Smithsonian Institution for the National Museum." In addition, "several entire State exhibits and many belonging to private parties" were donated. "Nevada, Montana, and Utah presented the whole of the mineral exhibits, while partial exhibits were received from several other States and Territories." It took sixty-six freight cars to bring it all from Philadelphia.

Before the end of 1876, Congress was asked for an appropriation of $250,000 for a new museum building. Action was not taken, however, until 1879. In the meantime, Secretary Henry died, and the task of seeing the new building through was one of the first devolving upon Baird as the new Secretary. The erection of the building, with General William T. Sherman as chairman of the building commission, was started on April 17, 1879, and completed, though still unoccupied, in 1881, in time for the inaugural reception and ball for President James A. Garfield on March 4. The structure, considered temporary when it was built, covered two and a third acres directly east of the Smithsonian Building and was built of red brick and Ohio sandstone. It was designed by Washington architects Cluss and Schulze in a modernized Romanesque style to blend with the neighboring Smithsonian Building. Its 1-story plan, approximately 325 feet square, provided a 135-foot-high central rotunda from which radiated four lofty naves with open balconies and connecting ranges. Per cubic foot of space, it was the cheapest building ever erected by the government in Washington.

Originally referred to as the "Annex to the Smithsonian Institution," the structure later became known as the National Museum Building and still later as the Arts and Industries Building. In the 1950's, during the Institution's program of exhibits renovation, many of the exhibition halls in the building were modernized and drew record crowds of visitors. The Power Hall, the Hall of the Gowns of the First Ladies of the White House, the Hall of Health, and others were fine examples of modern educational exhibits. When the Museum of History and Technology was opened in 1964, most of the arts and industries exhibits and departments were removed to it, and today the Arts and Industries Building is devoted to aeronautics, to temporary industrial and space-age exhibits, and to administration offices. All in all, the building has served its purposes long and well. Many of America's most famous treasures—the *Spirit of St. Louis,* the Wrights' *Kitty Hawk Flyer,* the original "Star-Spangled Banner," the *John Bull* locomotive, George Washington's uniform and field kit, to name just a few—have been displayed in it.

Today, the Arts and Industries Building is being phased into a new career as the Smithsonian Exposition Hall. It will provide a place for changing and experimental exhibits, sometimes directed toward social action, that are not a particular concern of the Institution's component museums and for traveling exhibitions of many kinds not related to the Smithsonian's own programs. The name of the building will not be changed until the space occupied therein by the National Air and Space Museum and other offices has been vacated.

THE NATURAL HISTORY BUILDING

Another quarter-century elapsed before the Institution got its third building, which for many years was known as the "new" National Museum. The "old" National Museum, built especially to house the Philadelphia Centennial influx of exhibition materials, soon began to bulge at the seams as the national collections in science, industry, and history continued to accumulate. The particular need was for a building to house the increasing collections of natural-history materials and to provide room for educational exhibits comparable to those of other great museums of the world. The new building, urged by Secretary Langley and his staff, promised to provide a safer depository for some of the real treasures of the American people in the realms of biology, anthropology, geology, and all the subdivisions thereof.

Congress finally provided funds to the Smithsonian for the erection of the new building, and ground was broken on June 15, 1904, at the foot of Tenth Street, N.W., on the south side of what is now Constitution Avenue. By the time the excavation and foundations were completed, however, Langley had died, and when the cornerstone was laid on October 15, 1906, the new Secretary, Charles D. Walcott, had taken over.

Monumental in scale, suited to the position it occupied in the capital's Mall, the building incorporated the latest developments in museum construction. The architects were Hornblower and Marshall of Washington. The building's design was classic, and the structure was finished on all sides in granite. The floor area of the four stories totaled more than 10 acres; the frontage measured 561 feet, the depth 365 feet, and the height 82 feet. An octagonal rotunda, 80 feet in diameter, with four massive stone piers and a curved tiled ceiling, reached a height of 124.5 feet. The building cost $3.5 million and was completed on June 20, 1911, although portions of it were opened to the public in March of the previous year.

It was a great day for the Smithsonian when the museum curators moved into their new offices and the cluttered collections and cramped exhibits could be reinstated in the commodious marble halls. For the first time since the Smithsonian was founded, there was room enough for both exhibition and study materials. Unfortunately, however, this situation did not last many years. The national collections in all departments of natural history continued to increase, and it was not until the early 1960's, after the exigencies of two world wars had taken their toll of the national budget, that Smithsonian appeals to Congress were heard and funds provided for new buildings.

In 1963, an east-wing extension of the Natural History Building was completed, and a matching west wing was ready for occupancy a couple of years later. The 6-story additions, measuring 199 by 180 feet, approximately doubled the floor area of the original building. The total area is now more than 20 acres. In addition to the exhibits in all the divisions of natural history, many of which were renovated and modernized during the decade from 1955 to 1965, the Natural History Building also housed the National Collection of Fine Arts until 1969, the large Smithsonian Library, and several accessory operations such as a taxidermy shop, the supply division, an auditorium, and exhibit workshops.

Today, the Natural History Building serves a triple function: it houses the voluminous study collections of animals, plants, fossils, and artifacts of human cultures that have become the property of the American people since even before the Smithsonian was founded and now number millions of specimens; it provides laboratories for the zoologists, botanists, archeologists, and paleontologists who spend their careers in scientific study of these collections; and it displays exhibits for the edification of the public. In its great halls, such as the Hall of Fossil Plants and Invertebrates, the Hall of the Age of Mammals, the Hall of Gems and Minerals, the Hall of the Native Peoples of the Americas, the American Indian Hall, the Hall of Ocean Life, visitors may view some of the finest modern natural-history exhibits of their kind.

THE MUSEUM OF HISTORY AND TECHNOLOGY

The Arts and Industries Building, though sprawling and capacious, was always crowded to the gunwales. Even from its beginning, with its overflow from the Philadelphia Centennial Exposition, it was inadequate to accommodate the growing collections and exhibits in the mechanical arts, invention, and industry that came to the Smithsonian. Nevertheless, it was many years before the dreams of the museum curators for new facilities were realized. In 1946, Frank A. Taylor, then curator of the National Museum's Division of Engineering and later director of the museum, wrote in *Scientific Monthly*:

> One day the United States will have a national museum of science, engineering, and industry, as most large nations have. Normally, it will be a part of the National Museum under the direction of the Smithsonian Institution and will be based in part upon the present extensive collections of the Smithsonian in these fields. Like all museums of the Smithsonian, this one will be a museum of record as well as of exhibition. As part of the National Museum, its scope will include all the sciences except natural history and all of engineering and industry, including agriculture.

The Taylor blueprint, with, of course, many changes and modifications, began to materialize in 1956, when Congress appropriated about $34 million for a new Museum of History and Technology for the Smithsonian. After elaborate architectural planning, ground was broken for the structure on

August 22, 1958. A little more than five years later, this great museum was completed. When it opened to the public on January 23, 1964, ten of the fifty exhibition halls were ready for visitors. Since then, more have been completed, but several more years will be required before all can be opened to the public. The work of amplifying exhibits and keeping them current is a continuing process.

The Museum of History and Technology, built to illustrate the cultural and technological development of the nation from colonial times, is located on the Mall directly west of the Natural History Building on Constitution Avenue between Twelfth and Fourteenth streets. Designed in a modified classical style by the New York architectural firm of McKim, Mead, & White (succeeded in 1956 by Steinmann, Cain, & White), the building measures 578 by 302 feet and is 121 feet high. It has become one of the finest showplaces in the capital. Three of its five main floors are devoted to exhibits, with offices, laboratories, and storage areas on the upper two. The basement contains a cafeteria opening on a sunken garden, service facilities and shops, and exhibits laboratories. In 1967, it drew 5,546,102 visitors, an average of over 15,000 a day, more than for any other Smithsonian building.

The Freer Building

The building for the Freer Gallery of Art was the Smithsonian's first edifice devoted solely to art. Built from funds arising from the philanthropy of the wealthy Detroit art connoisseur and businessman Charles Lang Freer, it is one of the acknowledged architectural gems of the capital. It is located just west of the "castle" on the south side of the Mall at Twelfth Street and Jefferson Drive, S.W., its back to Independence Avenue. The building's architect was Charles A. Platt of New York. As public buildings go, it is not large: it measures only 228 by 185 feet and has but two main floors. The Florentine Renaissance palace style in which it is designed seems eminently satisfying and suitable, dignified yet unpretentious. The outside stone is a pink granite quarried near Milford, Massachusetts. Eighteen interconnecting galleries of various sizes surround a central court about 65 feet square, which is faced with Tennessee marble. The court, where at one time peacocks strutted, is open to the sky and laid out with walks, gardens, and fountains. In the exhibition halls on the upper floor are shown the Freer collection of paintings and sculpture from the Middle East, India, and the Orient. Also displayed are works by American artists such as John Singer Sargent and Winslow Homer, and the Peacock Room that James Whistler painted for the Frederick Leyland house in London. The lower floor, at ground level, is devoted to the administrative offices, laboratories and studios, an auditorium, storage rooms, and a library that has become over the years one of the nation's most precious reference collections of books, periodicals, and manuscripts devoted principally to Oriental art.

Ground was broken for the Freer Building on September 23, 1916, but because of construction delays occasioned principally by the country's being at war, the gallery was not completed until the spring of 1921, over four years after the laying of the cornerstone. By the time the building was finally opened to the public on May 2, 1923, Freer had died, but the collections had been received from the executors of the Freer estate and installed under the direction of the gallery's first director, John Ellerton Lodge. As William Henry Holmes wrote in a comment at the time of Freer's death, "The building and collections represent an outlay of some six or seven million dollars and constitute one of the most important and valued donations which any individual has ever made freely and unconditionally to the Nation."

MELLON'S MARBLE HALLS

Thirty years after Freer's gift was made to the Smithsonian, another multimillionaire, Andrew W. Mellon, presented his priceless art collection and the sum of $15 million to the nation for a National Gallery of Art, to be administered by the Smithsonian Institution. The gift was accepted by act of Congress on March 24, 1937, and soon after the building began to rise on the Mall, on Constitution Avenue between Seventh and Fourth streets. It was opened to the public on March 17, 1941, at impressive ceremonies led by President Franklin Delano Roosevelt.

Designed in the classical style by the architect John Russell Pope, the National Gallery is one of the largest marble structures in the world, covering more than half a million square feet of floor space, with about 238,000 square feet for exhibition purposes. It is built of rose-white Tennessee marble and measures approximately 829 by 350 feet. The interior of the rotunda and of the east and west sculpture halls are of Alabama Rockwood stone. Each of the two garden courts, of Indiana limestone, has a colonnade of 15 monoliths and in the center a fountain. Columns of dark-green Italian marble surround the rotunda, which has a dome rising almost 150 feet. The flooring of the exhibition halls is American fumed oak.

HOUSING AIR AND SPACE

The "temporary" steel hangarlike Air and Space Building on Independence Avenue at Tenth Street, S.W., was erected in 1917 and was used by the U.S. Signal Service during World War I as a testing laboratory for the Liberty aircraft engine. Acquired by the Smithsonian in November, 1919, it was opened to the public on October 7, 1920, to exhibit aircraft and accessories produced during the war. It contains about 14,000 square feet of floor space and today it is occupied by a portion of the National Air and Space Museum collections.

A new building for the National Air and Space Museum, long needed to accommodate and adequately display the national aeronautical collections, was authorized by Congress in June, 1966, after several years of consideration, but funds to construct the museum have not yet been appropriated. The site for the building, in the southeast portion of the Mall, has been chosen and approved. The building has been designed by Gyo Obata of the St. Louis architectural firm of Hellmuth, Obata, and Kassabaum, and is estimated to cost in the neighborhood of $50 million. It will be the first building of its size— 784 by 250 feet and containing over 1 million square feet of floor space—designed especially to house exhibits tracing the principles and evolution of air and space flight. Its construction of textured stone, glass, and anodized aluminum is intended to harmonize with neighboring buildings. By combining glass walls with exhibit areas suspended at various levels between great columns, the architect has created an effective spaciousness appropriate to the large aircraft, space vehicles, and rocket boosters it is to house. At the same time, the building will provide areas for exhibiting the many small objects important in aerospace development. As projected, the museum will also contain a library, laboratories, and study facilities appropriate to its intended use as a research center for curators and visiting scholars studying the history and technology of flight.

THE ZOO BUILDINGS

Remodeling of the buildings of the National Zoological Park, located in Rock Creek Park, just over two miles north of the White House, has been in progress since 1963.

The first of the buildings to be renovated was the Bird House, originally built in 1928 from plans by District of Columbia municipal architect Albert Harris. First of the new buildings was the Great Flight Cage, a spectacular structure designed by Richard E. Dimon of Washington and opened in 1965. It adjoins the remodeled Bird House. Both feature walk-through exhibits in which visitors can come close to birds in a natural surrounding—a hummingbird, for example, has been seen sitting on a visitor's head.

The second phase of the renovation program, new shelters for the hoofed stock, was completed and opened in stages in 1966.

Among the other buildings scheduled for renovation are the Lion House, which sheltered the entire animal collection when built in 1890, and the Monkey House, designed in 1904 for small mammals and opened in 1906. Others are the Reptile House, built in 1930 from designs by Albert Harris and opened in 1931, and the Elephant and Small Mammal Houses, built in 1937, from designs by Edwin Clark, architect for Chicago's Brookfield Zoo.

Oldest of the zoo's buildings is Holt Mansion, a historic house used as the administrative offices. Built in 1805, it once served as Andrew Jackson's summer refuge; it was acquired with the land for the National Zoological Park when the zoo was established in Rock Creek valley in 1890—the same year that the surrounding Rock Creek Park was created. The house is now designated as a national historic landmark.

GALLERIES FOR THE FINE ARTS

Among the monumental buildings in Washington, only the White House and Capitol antedate the Old Patent Office Building, now thoroughly renovated and rejuvenated to accommodate two Smithsonian art museums, the National Collection of Fine Arts and the National Portrait Gallery.

Constructed of marble, granite, and sandstone from Maine, Massachusetts, Connecticut, Maryland, and Virginia, the building stands four stories high and measures 413 by 280 feet over all, with an elm-shaded central court 270 by 112 feet in size.

The building's history is both interesting and complex. At the time of its completion in 1867, it was the largest building in the United States, and, according to some architectural critics, it still remains one of the most distinguished. It is situated in the central Washington block bounded south and north by F and G streets, east and west by Seventh and Ninth streets, on a site earlier designated by Pierre Charles L'Enfant for a national "Pantheon," and it was built a wing at a time between 1836 and 1867. Five architects—William Parker Eliot, Ithiel Town, Robert Mills, Thomas U. Walter, and Edward Clark—contributed successively to its Greek Revival design. Construction details reflect changing practices in such things as vaulting, re-enforcing floors and roofs, and fireproofing—matters that were tested in 1877 when fire destroyed the top floors of the east and north wings.

The Patent Office moved into the south wing when it was completed in 1840, and the national collections of objects of art, manufacture, natural history, and foreign curios were housed in the building until 1857, when they were transferred to the Smithsonian. The upper floor was used to display patent models as well as the national collections in an exhibition hall that extended 1,062 feet around the entire quadrangle. The final wing, completed in 1867, was taken over by the military during the Civil War (Patent Office copyist Clara Barton cared for the wounded in the hospital there), and it was the scene of President Lincoln's second inaugural ball on March 4, 1865. Various offices and bureaus of the Department of the Interior shared the building with the Patent Office from 1847 to 1917. In 1932, the U.S. Civil Service Commission took it over.

After the Commission moved to a new building, use of the old Patent Office Building to house the National Collection of Fine Arts and the National Portrait Gallery was authorized by Congress in 1958. The building was transferred to the Smithsonian Institution in 1963. Renovation was started in 1964 and completed in 1968, in which year its galleries, restored to their original function, were once again open to the public, this time with displays devoted to the fine arts. The architects for the extensive renovation were the Washington firm Faulkner, Kingsbury, and Stenhouse.

THE KENNEDY CENTER

The contributions of private citizens, matched by federal appropriations and magnificently supplemented by gifts from foreign governments, have been combined to create the John F. Kennedy Center for the Performing Arts as a national memorial to the late President. Rising in a 17.5-acre park on the east bank of the Potomac River, the building was designed by the American architect Edward Durell Stone. Groundbreaking ceremonies were held on December 2, 1964. Completion is expected in 1970.

When finished, the Kennedy Center building will measure 630 by 300 feet and will be faced with Carrara marble. A grand foyer will extend the entire length of the river front, along which a glass wall will rise to the ceiling. Opening onto it will be a concert hall, an opera hall, and a theater, with proposed seating capacities of 2,700, 2,200, and 1,100, respectively. At one end of the roof terrace will be two large restaurants and, at the other, a studio playhouse. Connecting them will be an atrium gallery, a 225-by-40-foot exhibition and reception area through the center of the roof terrace. A 1,600-car underground garage with access to surrounding parkways will be provided.

THE RENWICK GALLERY

The Renwick Gallery stands near the White House on Pennsylvania Avenue at the northeast corner of Seventeenth Street. Originally designed by the architect of the Smithsonian Building, James Renwick, Jr., to house the collection of paintings and art objects that W. W. Corcoran, a wealthy Washington banker and philanthropist, had presented to the city of Washington, it is reputedly this country's first building in the French Renaissance revival style of architecture and the first built especially as an art gallery. Measuring 104 by 124.5 feet, it is constructed of brick, with trimmings of Belleville freestone.

Construction began in 1857, but the unfinished building was taken over in 1861 by Montgomery C. Meigs, quartermaster general of the Union Army, to house his staff and supplies. It was returned to the trustees of the Corcoran Gallery in 1869 and was opened to the public after construction was completed in 1874. It was occupied by the Corcoran until 1897, when the gallery moved to its present home nearby.

Purchased by the government in 1901, the building housed the U.S. Court of Claims from 1899 until 1964. It was turned over to the Smithsonian Institution in 1966 and is presently being renovated for the display and study of American arts, crafts, and design.

THE HIRSHHORN GALLERY

The Hirshhorn Museum and Sculpture Garden, designed by Gordon Bunshaft of the New York architectural firm of Skidmore, Owings and Merrill, will be constructed on a 12-acre Mall site between Seventh and Ninth streets, S.W., and between Independence Avenue and Madison Drive. It will be a circular building 231 feet in diameter, with three floors rising 82 feet above ground, facing on a rectangular outdoor sculpture garden extending across the Mall from Jefferson Drive to Madison Drive.

The main feature of the building design is the exposed concrete structural form consisting of four main columns supporting the underside of the first floor, 14 feet above the Mall. Above, the windowless exterior wall will be surfaced with marble. The Sculpture Garden, depressed below the surface of the Mall, will have walls also of marble and a pool 80 feet wide and 430 feet long.

The building is a gift to the nation from Joseph Hirshhorn of New York and was accepted by Congress for the Smithsonian November 7, 1966. Ground was broken for the building on January 8, 1969, but actual construction was delayed until federal funds were released.

X

The Smithsonian's Finances
and Friends

The flexibility of Smithsonian fiscal operations arises from the fact that its funds derive from two sources—one governmental, the other private. In fact, the Institution is one of the very few federal agencies having the authority to accept private, nongovernmental funds. The advantages of this arrangement are apparent. However, the fiscal administration of the Smithsonian is not so simple as it might seem, for the accounting of the private funds and that of the government funds must be kept separate.

In the *Congressional Directory*, the Smithsonian is listed as one of the independent agencies of the federal government, indicating that although the government has not integrated the Institution into the departmental system—and cannot under the law—it keeps a watchful eye over its ward. The Instituition oversees the expenditure of government funds because Congress entrusts to its care several public bureaus that developed from the private initiative of the Smithsonian. In spite of this close and mutually profitable relationship, the Smithsonian regards itself as essentially a private establishment.

THE PRIVATE SIDE

The so-called parent fund of the Smithsonian, comprised of the original Smithson bequest plus subsequent accretions, amounts to $1 million. Smithson's gift was "lent to the United States Treasury at 6 per centum per annum interest," and by congressional act of March 12, 1894, the Secretary of the Treasury was "authorized to receive into the Treasury, on the same terms . . . such sums as the regents may, from time to time see fit to deposit, not exceeding, with the original bequest the sum of $1,000,000." This amount was reached in 1917. Thus the perpetual income from the parent fund is now $60,000 per annum.

In addition to the parent fund, approximately $10 million in capital funds has been accumulated and invested. The major portion is carried on the Institution's books as the so-called Consolidated Fund, which falls into two categories: (1) funds (in 1968 amounting to approximately $4 million) the income from which is available for the unrestricted use of the Institution and (2) funds (approximately $5 million) whose income is restricted, usually by the donors, to specific uses. The Freer Gallery of Art Fund, also accounted for separately, which originated in the 1906 gift of Charles L. Freer to establish and maintain the gallery, had by the end of fiscal year 1967 reached the sum of slightly more than $12.1 million. Added to the other invested endowments of the Institution, it brought the total to approximately $23 million.

In connection with one gift, some have felt that Secretary Walcott and the regents may have muffed the ball. In 1912, Dr. Frederick G. Cottrell, chemist of the U.S. Bureau of Mines, offered the Smithsonian his patents "relating to the electrical precipitation of dust, smoke, and chemical fumes." The gift, however, was not accepted for the Institution. Instead, a separate organization, the Research Corporation of New York, was established to administer the funds accruing for the benefit of research. The objects of the corporation are:

First, to acquire inventions and patents and to make them more available in the arts and industries, while using them as a source of income, and, second, to apply all profits derived from such use to the advancement of technical and scientific investigation and experimentation through the agency of the Smithsonian Institution and such other scientific and educational institutions and societies as may be selected by the directors.

In the years since 1912, the income of the corporation has been built up and large grants have been made for research. The Smithsonian has received considerable sums from the corporation, and the Secretary is an ex officio member of the corporation's board of directors, but hindsight suggests what the generous Cottrell gift would have meant to the Smithsonian if it had been placed under its direct control.

In his memoir of Secretary Walcott, Ellis L. Yochelson suggested that the decision of the Board of Regents not to involve the Smithsonian directly in the enterprise, but to organize a separate stock corporation "in which the Institution would be represented by the Secretary as an individual and not in his capacity as Secretary," was made only after due deliberation:

> It was Dr. Cottrell's hope that he could turn his patent rights over to the Smithsonian Institution "for the purpose of creating a fund from the business development of these patents which could be used for research to carry forward not only these special lines, but any lines of human endeavor." Unconfirmed reports have it that William Howard Taft [then President of the United States] rendered the legal opinion, right or wrong, as to the inappropriateness of the Smithsonian's holding the patents and suggested the formation of a stock company, which eventually became the Research Corporation.

As institutional endowments go these days, $23 million is not a large sum, a fact that belies the popular belief that the Smithsonian is a rich institution. The great wonder is that over the long haul it has done so much with so little. On this point, A. Hunter Dupree in his book *Science in the Federal Govern-*

ment (Cambridge, Mass.: Harvard University Press, 1957) commented:

> The original [Smithsonian] endowment had been twice as large as Yale's, larger than those of Princeton, Columbia, and the University of Pennsylvania, and equal to Harvard's. In 1901 the secretary stated that the "Institution's endowment has in . . . fifty years increased but from $600,000 to somewhat less than $1,000,000, but the *average* endowment of the five universities named is now about $8,000,000, indicating that in this regard the Institution's fund for scientific purposes is relatively unimportant compared with what it was fifty years ago." For such small means to make a measurable impression on the course of scientific research required ever more difficult selectivity in the choice of objectives.

Expenditure of Smithsonian funds is vested in the Secretary by authority of the Board of Regents, whose executive committee yearly makes and publishes a duly audited financial report. The immediate financial deputy is the Smithsonian treasurer. The endowment funds, other than the 6 per cent U.S. Treasury deposit, are invested in stocks and bonds, real estate, and mortgages.

The annual income on $23 million, even at an optimum rate of 6 per cent, is only $1.4 million, which is not enough to finance the many projects and affairs of the Smithsonian. The balance required is made up from three principal sources: (1) federal funds appropriated directly to the Institution by Congress for prescribed purposes; (2) funds received by transfer or grant from other agencies of the U.S. Government to carry on specific programs, sometimes by contract; and (3) grants and gifts from foundations and individuals, usually for specific programs and projects. The last every year number several hundred, ranging in amount from a few dollars to sizable sums. To mention a few recent examples: in 1967, a grant of $40,000 was received from the Morris and Gwendolyn Cafritz Foundation toward the purchase of a stabile designed by Alexander Calder; $25,000 was received from the Daniel and Florence Guggenheim Foundation for a commemorative Guggenheim exhibit, a Guggenheim lecture, and fellowships for graduate research at the National Air and Space Museum; $45,000 was given by the National Geographic Society for seven research projects; $80,000 came from the Max C. Fleischmann Foundation of Nevada and the Old Dominion Foundation for the Institution's Chesapeake Bay Center for Field Biology; $100,000 was received from the Research Corporation of New York for the Smithsonian's Ivy Neck properties; $16,785 was given by the Kevorkian Foundation for the publication of a work on Indian sculptures in the Freer Gallery of Art; $10,500 was received from the Wenner-Gren Foundation for two research projects in cultural anthropology; and gifts were received from individuals too numerous to list here.

A few of the more interesting and substantial gifts and bequests of past years, which have served to build up the Smithsonian endowment funds, deserve mention.

Quite characteristically, the earliest addition to the Smithson fund came from Joseph Henry himself. In 1847, the College of New Jersey (Princeton University) paid him $1,000 for a course of lectures he delivered at the college, and he promptly turned the money over "to the credit of the Board of Regents." In 1874, another $1,000 was bequeathed by James Hamilton, a philanthropic and public-spirited lawyer of Carlisle, Pennsylvania. Five years later Dr. Simeon Habel, an Austrian-born traveler and authority on the sculptures of Santa Lucia Cosumalwhuapa in Guatemala, bequeathed $402.59 to the Smithsonian, which added $97.41 from its own funds to raise the sum to an even $500, and added it to the Smithson parent fund.

In 1890, the Institution received $5,000 each from Dr. Jerome H. Kidder, a naturalist and surgeon and, in late life, a staff member of the Smithsonian, and Alexander Graham Bell, a Smithsonian regent, for astrophysical research. Their gifts were critical in the establishment of the Astrophysical Observatory.

The first six-figure post-Smithson gift did not come until Secretary Langley's administration. In 1891, Thomas George Hodgkins, a prosperous, devout, London-born businessman then living in Setauket, Long Island, gave the then munificent sum of $200,000 to the Smithsonian, half of which he wished to be used for "the investigation of the properties of atmospheric air." Hodgkins himself had made a longtime study of the atmosphere in relation to human well-being and had come to believe, as Langley recorded, that "most of the physical evils to which mankind are subject arise from the vitiation of the air which they breathe, and that the study of the atmosphere is not unimportant even with relation to man's moral and spiritual, as well as his physical, health." After Hodgkins's death in 1892, the Institution received from his estate an additional sum of nearly $50,000. In 1893, to memorialize the donor, Langley announced the establishment of the Hodgkins Medal to be awarded "for important contributions to our knowledge of the nature and properties of atmospheric air or for practical applications of our existing knowledge of them to the welfare of mankind." The medal was first bestowed in 1899 upon Professor James (later Sir) Dewar, British chemist; three years later on another Englishman, Professor J. J. Thomson, eminent atomic physicist; and not again until 1965, when it was awarded to Dr. Joseph Kaplan, geophysicist and meteorologist of the University of California at Los Angeles.

In 1901, Joseph White Sprague bequeathed to the Institution $200,000 (about 40 per cent of his estate) to be known as the Sprague Fund and used for the advancement of the physical sciences. The principal of this fund today amounts to about $2 million.

John A. Roebling, grandson and son of the Roebling engineers who built the Brooklyn Bridge, was a longtime Smithsonian benefactor and from time to time gave the Institution well over half a million dollars for the work of the Astrophysical Observatory, for Dr. Abbot's solar research, and for the care, improvement, and increase of the collection of gems and minerals that Roebling had donated to the Institution in memory of his father.

In 1922, Secretary Charles D. Walcott and his wife Mary Vaux Walcott established a fund for the development of geological and paleontological studies and publications; the initial gift was $11,520. When Mrs. Walcott died in 1940, she left $400,000 to the Institution to be added to the fund, which today has grown to about $1 million.

In 1931, the Smithsonian endowment was augmented by a $100,000 bequest from Dwight W. Morrow, who had been U.S. Ambassador to Mexico, a U.S. Senator, and a regent of the Institution. In 1938, Annie-May Hegeman, as a memorial to her father, Henry Kirke Porter, offered the Smithsonian half the proceeds of the sale of her property, amounting to about $600,000. This fund, unrestricted in use, today totals about $500,000. Approximately $130,000 was received in 1940 from the estate of Eleanor E. Witherspoon to found the Thomas W. Witherspoon Memorial, on the condition that none of the income should be used in collecting birds and animals dead or alive or for purposes of vivisection. Another sizable unrestricted bequest came in 1963 from Robert Lee Forrest, of Baltimore, Maryland. By 1968, the principal of this gift was valued at nearly $2 million. The beneficences of Charles L. Freer, Andrew W. Mellon, and Joseph H. Hirshhorn in establishing art galleries under the Smithsonian have been mentioned elsewhere.

Thus, the Smithsonian has not been without many friends, especially in the field of art, but efforts on the part of the

Institution to increase its endowments have been sporadic and by no means overwhelming.

THE GOVERNMENT'S CONTRIBUTION

To run the strictly government business and operate the bureaus and offices that Congress has authorized and directed be administered by the Smithsonian, federal funds are annually appropriated. In this regard, the Institution operates like any government department. It must present an annual budget, which runs a double gantlet: the agency first submits its budget to the Bureau of the Budget, an adjunct of the Office of the President, and justifies its requests in detail; it must then justify the amounts included in the President's budget before Congress through the appropriations committees in the House of Representatives and in the Senate.

The budgetary process is long and costly, seemingly wasteful of time, and often frustrating, but unquestionably necessary in the interests of good government. Unfortunately, in ironing out differences between Senate-passed and House-passed versions of an appropriation bill, whole programs can be slashed out summarily without further reference to the department involved, and then the department must try to get the items restored in a "deficiency" bill or start the process all over again the next year. The budget system no doubt encourages foresight and planning, but it has weaknesses, particularly in tending to make agencies overestimate their needs to offset later cuts.

The Smithsonian Institution's budget, of course, is only an infinitesimal part of that of the total government's. In recent years, as a matter of expediency, the Smithsonian's appropriation request has been tacked onto that of the Department of the Interior as a separate item when presented to Congress.

In the decade from 1957 to 1967, the federal appropriations for the Smithsonian multiplied fivefold, not counting funds for construction of new buildings. This increment was due to expansion and increase of the Institution's activities and programs as well as to general upward inflationary trends. The change can be best shown by a tabular comparison of how the Smithsonian funds were allocated during the two years 1957 and 1967.

Funds appropriated to the Institution for its regular operations for the fiscal year ended June 30, 1957, were obligated as follows:

Management	$ 81,010
U.S. National Museum	1,782,690
Bureau of American Ethnology	61,891
Astrophysical Observatory	302,510
National Collection of Fine Arts	48,185
National Air Museum	120,156
International Exchange Service	87,513
Canal Zone Biological Area	30,274
Maintenance and operation of buildings	1,442,364
Other general services	467,562
Unobligated balance	845
Total	$4,425,000

For the fiscal year ended June 30, 1967, the funds obligated were:

Astrophysical Observatory	$ 1,638,000
Education and training	342,000
Freer Gallery of Art	34,000
International activities	60,000
International Exchange Service	128,000
National Air and Space Museum	454,000
National Armed Forces Museum Advisory Board	125,000
National Collection of Fine Arts	677,000
National Portrait Gallery	449,000
Office of Ecology	118,000
Office of Oceanography and Limnology	268,000

Radiation Biology Laboratory	394,000
Tropical Research Institute	304,000
U.S. National Museum	7,504,000
Research awards	400,000
Office of the Secretary	369,000
Management support	432,000
Buildings Management Department	6,648,000
Administrative services	2,344,000
Unobligated balance	42,000
Total	$22,730,000

These figures do not include funds that came to the Institution indirectly by transfer from other government agencies. For example, in 1957 there were transferred $720,000 from the District of Columbia for the operation of the National Zoological Park (an awkward though long-standing arrangement) and $108,500 from the National Park Service, Department of the Interior, for the river basin surveys. Comparable figures for 1967 were $2 million for the National Zoological Park and $219,000 for the river basin surveys. Neither do the foregoing tabular figures include appropriations made to the National Gallery of Art, which in 1967 amounted to $2.8 million, inasmuch as the gallery, though legally a Smithsonian bureau, is administered by a separate board of trustees.

Funds also come to the Institution by grants from federal agencies for specific research projects. A number of agencies have large budgets for vast research programs, which in many cases have to be carried out, in part at least, by outside contract. Smithsonian specialized facilities and the scientific expertise of its staff are frequently so requisitioned. It is a mutually beneficial practice, and many millions of dollars from such sources have been directed into the Smithsonian's financial bloodstream—particularly in the years since the U.S. space programs gained momentum, the National Science Foundation was established, and the government began to sponsor large-scale research in the basic sciences. Some of the agencies that have made sizable grants to the Smithsonian to carry out portions of their research programs have been the National Aeronautics and Space Administration, the National Science Foundation, the U.S. Air Force, the U.S. Army, the Office of Naval Research, the Department of the Interior, the Atomic Energy Commission, and the Department of Health, Education, and Welfare.

Another source of federal funds in very recent years has been the excess currencies deriving from the sale of surplus agricultural commodities under P.L. 480. In 1967, a total of $2.3 million was granted to the Smithsonian in foreign currencies for museum programs and related research. These projects are carried out in the so-called excess-currency countries. (See Office of International Activities, Chapter VIII.)

The process of getting money out of Congress is not without its lighter moments. So far as the Smithsonian is concerned, I have a feeling that chairmen of congressional appropriations committees have frequently looked forward to hearings involving Smithsonian requests as a welcome relief from the more prosaic subjects and astronomical figures they ordinarily must deal with. Back in Secretary Langley's day, one of the most eloquent budgetary experts in Congress was the Honorable Joseph G. Cannon of Illinois, known as Uncle Joe, who in his long and colorful career in the House of Representatives certainly had a greater and more varied experience in government budget-making than any other American up to his time, and perhaps since. In an article in *Harper's* in October, 1919, Uncle Joe related an incident involving a Smithsonian request:

I have some impressive memories of Government experts who did not understand the art of propaganda. There was Prof. Langley, for many years secretary of the Smithsonian Institution. He was a great scientist and one of the most modest men about asking for Government help that I ever met. About 20 years ago, when I was chairman of the Committee on Appropriations, Prof. Langley was before the committee, and after he had presented his estimates to the subcommittee I asked if there was anything else he would like to present to the committee.

"Yes, Mr. Chairman; I would like to have $10,000 to experiment in building a flying machine," said the professor.

"Great Heavens!" I exclaimed. "A flying machine to ride up in the air?"

"Yes," he replied, "I don't wonder at your question because you have not given the subject any investigation. But is not a bird heavier than air? Is not the eagle who soars in the sunlight and above the clouds heavier than air; and don't you think we could devise a machine by which the human animal can navigate the air?"

He did not have to argue or make elaborate explanations. The subcommittee agreed to the appropriation, the full committee accepted the recommendation, and the House and Senate made the appropriation; and I was more ridiculed and abused for "wasting the people's money" on flying machines than for any other appropriation I reported while chairman of that committee. I was cartooned as Mother Shipton riding through the air on a broom, and was given no end of notoriety because of that modest appropriation. Prof. Langley built his machine, took it down the Potomac and made it fly, but he was too old to operate it himself, and his assistant was too timid, especially with a bevy of newspaper correspondents hovering about to record the failure, and the flying machine, after a very short flight, tumbled into the river. The gasolene engine had not been fully developed and Langley failed, but the Wright brothers took up the same principle and, with a better engine, made flying not only a possibility but developed it into a pastime. . . . But Langley was an exception among Government experts, especially in his modesty about asking for big Government appropriations, and my confidence in him made me more lenient in considering the extravagant prospectuses of others.

Secretary Abbot, in the *Cosmos Club Bulletin* of September, 1957, told the story of another occasion, on which Uncle Joe was listening to a hearing before the House Appropriations Committee:

> We used to go up to Congress to argue for the appropriations for the various Government branches administered by the Smithsonian. In 1910, after the successful rebellion of Representative Norris of Nebraska had defeated the Old Guard of Republicans, the House had gone Democratic. At our hearing the new chairman of the Appropriations Committee, Representative Fitzgerald of Brooklyn, said, "The next item is the Astrophysical Observatory. What is the Astrophysical Observatory? What good is it? What has it done?" Secretary Walcott said, "Mr. Abbot will speak to that, Mr. Chairman." So I began to testify, but the chairman was called out of the room.
>
> Representative Sherley of Kentucky said, "Well, this is rather interesting, but I fear Fitz will have his troubles if he tries to tell about it on the floor of the House." Uncle Joe Cannon, who had been dethroned as Speaker, and was now back on the Appropriations Committee, of which he had been a shining head for a generation, was walking to and fro in his long black coat, with his cigar vertical in the corner of his mouth. He stopped opposite Sherley and said, "No, Sherley. I rekilect when old Perfesser Langley came to me and said, 'I need $4,000 for the Astrophysical Observatory.' 'But Perfesser,' said I, 'can't you reduce that?' 'No,' said he, 'I have to investigate the infrared spectrum of the sun with the bolometer.' 'My God,' said I, 'can't you abolish that?' But no, Sherley, I don't care a damn about the stars that are so far away it takes a thousand years for light to come from 'em, and if they were all abolished tonight our great-grand-children would never know the difference. I don't care a damn about the stars, but everything hangs on the sun, Sherley, and it ought to be investigated. I think the appropriation is all right!"

Another appropriations story, told by the late director of the National Zoological Park, Dr. William M. Mann, in his book *Wild Animals in and out of the Zoo,* involved a mynah bird that attained considerable notoriety.

Our most noted bird was brought to us from Java by Dr. H. C. Kellers of the Navy, who was then surgeon to an astronomical expedition. When the bird was secured it could speak a sentence or two in Javanese. The sailors aboard the transport increased its vocabulary somewhat, and then some unknown person at the Zoo put on the final touch. The Smithsonian Institution held a conference to which the President and his Cabinet came, with the Board of Regents and other most consequential people, to listen to speeches and to visit small booths, each containing an exhibit from one of the branches of the Institution. The Zoo booth contained a rare small mammal or two, a pen of turtles, a tank of frogs, and the Javanese mynah as one of the bird exhibits. When the speeches were over, the party broke up to look at the collections, and as no less a person than the Director of the Budget, General H. M. Lord himself, entered the Zoo booth, the mynah asked him with perfect clarity, "How about the appropriation?"

There was just the proper amount of irritation in his voice, and the General turned and asked, "Who educated that bird?"

The bird reiterated, "How about the appropriation?"

The General, visibly nonplussed, and perhaps dismayed also at the sight of newspaper reporters snapping lead pencils in their hurry to take notes, turned to a friend and remarked, "That is impertinent," to which the mynah rejoined, "So's your old man."

We of the Zoo were, of course, deeply humiliated at this unseemly conduct on the part of one of our charges, but the story became one of the General's favorites.

An animal dealer heard the bird one day, and turned to me to say, "That is a two-hundred-dollar bird." The month before we had received an appropriation of $30,000, and even as he mentioned his paltry idea of the value of the bird we could hear the activities of workmen on the outside of the bird house, preparing ground to install outdoor cages, amply provided for by the new appropriation.

The relations between Congress and the Smithsonian have always been friendly. Congressmen have respected the traditions and objectives of the Institution, and many have been proud to serve on its Board of Regents, in which capacity they have been in a position to aid the Smithsonian in numerous ways. It was no drawback, for example, that the chairman of the House Appropriations Committee, the late Clarence Cannon, was a Smithsonian regent for many years. Though often showing a certain proprietary interest in the Smithsonian, congressmen have not been inclined to interfere with the activities of the Institution. Smithsonian officials, in turn, knowing where their bread and butter come from, try conscientiously to supply congressmen prompt information when requested, soft-pedal any lobbying proclivities, send the legislators and their constituents reports and publications, and, in general, aim to please. Their perennial hope is that some morning they will wake up to find that Congress has given them all the money they have asked for to carry out their expanding museum programs, render increased services to the public, and meet the ever broadening needs of research and the diffusion of knowledge that they have taken as their Smithsonian province. But that, of course, is wishful thinking.

XI

Quo Vadimus?

Of all the books that have been written about the Smithsonian Institution—and there have been many in its century and a quarter of existence—none has been able to tell the whole story. Each has told it in a different way, from a different point of view, for a different audience. That this is so testifies to the inexhaustible nature of the living organism that was born of James Smithson's dream. The leading question, of course, is simply this: Have the express wishes of Smithson been faithfully carried out? Would he be disappointed were he to see the Smithsonian today? It is an interesting thought to ponder.

The course of the Smithsonian has not been one long continuous success. There have been upward and downward curves; there have been failures and mistakes; but the solid achievements have justified Joseph Henry's and his successors' ambitions to make the Smithsonian, and keep it, one of the leading cultural institutions of the world. In great part, it was due to the persistence of the founding fathers, particularly John Quincy Adams and Joseph Henry, that the course was so firmly charted. As Wilcomb E. Washburn stated in his introduction to the John Quincy Adams lectures published by the Smithsonian in 1965:

The responsibility laid upon the United States by James Smithson to found an institution in Washington for "the in-

218

crease and diffusion of knowledge among men" was met. A
bridge between the eighteenth and twentieth centuries was
built. A dying man's charge was honored. An unborn genera-
tion's needs were anticipated.

LOOKING BACK

To enumerate all the Institution's achievements would be
to repeat a good deal that has already been covered in previous chapters, but the highlights may well be reviewed before
looking ahead.

During the first three decades, the period of Joseph Henry's
Secretaryship, the Smithsonian filled a pioneering role in
American science in which Henry himself was a dominant
figure. The accomplishments during this period were in large
part projections of his own energies, talents, and convictions.
For example, his deep interest in meteorology led to the inau-
guration of a system of meteorological observations, reported
by telegraph, by volunteer observers throughout the country
—the first system of systematic weather reporting probably
anywhere in the world. Another project close to Henry's
heart was the system of international exchange of scientific
literature, which is still an important Smithsonian activity.

With the help of Baird, there began in 1850 the Smithsonian's program of exploration, which became and still remains
world renowned. Exploration has been a continuing activity,
with outstanding results. Every continent and large island
group has been visited by numerous Smithsonian expeditions,
resulting in thousands of pages of Smithsonian and other
publications, millions of natural-history specimens for study
and exhibition, and inestimable new knowledge of peoples
and places. The total number of Smithsonian expeditions
would be difficult now to count, but from 1910 to 1940 they
were recorded and summarized in the annual illustrated
series Smithsonian Exploration Pamphlets. During that 30-

year period, the Institution sent out or participated in 709 field expeditions. Projected on this basis, the total number for the entire life of the Institution to the present would be at least two thousand, a conservative estimate. One of the most illustrious of Smithsonian-aided expeditions was that of John Wesley Powell down the Colorado River in 1869. Another was the Theodore Roosevelt African Expedition of 1909, which notably enriched the Institution's biological collections and exhibits.

Another great pride of Henry and Baird was the publication program they initiated. Here again, it was a venture that filled a gap in scientific service in this country, for in 1846 the media for the publication of large scientific monographs, particularly with adequate illustrations, were few and far between. The Smithsonian's publication program has probably done more than any other of the activities to enhance the Institution's world-wide reputation.

The development of the U.S. National Museum within the framework of the Smithsonian was Baird's special concern. Henry supported it, though not enthusiastically. Under them, it became one of the world's greatest museums. It has demanded more of the Smithsonian's attention, funds, and concern than has any of its other activities, until today it sometimes seems as if the tail wags the dog—which is what Henry feared. Be that as it may, the Smithsonian now has half a dozen museums attached to it in one way or another, and it has done an impressive job with them. It has found museum exhibition to be an effective and entertaining way to diffuse knowledge. And it has found that its vast collections in all branches of natural history, cultural history, and technology, made available for research, form a unique resource for a basic type of organized science.

In one particular branch of museum research—taxonomy —the Smithsonian has shone from the very start. Over the years, the National Museum became the principal national center for taxonomic research in zoology, botany, and paleontology. Today, with its enormous aggregations of specimens accumulated from all parts of the world, it is often thought of as a "bureau of standards" of natural history. As soon as collections of any sort are made, they must be systematically identified and classified if they are to be of use. Though other museums throughout the world also have great collections, the Smithsonian for more than a hundred years has taken the lead in the study, classification, and publication of descriptions of new forms of animals, plants, and fossils, often at times when it was difficult to obtain funds for this type of exacting and unromantic investigation. Many modern biologists regard taxonomy as a necessary evil and an intellectual plaything that may be disappearing, since theoretically all the forms of animals and plants will one day be discovered, named, and classified. The systematists, however, believe that they will never run out of a job and, more importantly, that taxonomy is indispensable to biology. I tend to come down on the side of the systematists and think that the eminent ecologist Paul B. Sears summed up the argument well in his biography of Charles Darwin:

> The increasing refinement of biological study requires greater certainty than ever before of the identity of animals and plants used in experimental work. The fact that all organisms are now considered to be part of one great family tree is a challenge to the intelligence and skill of the classifier who must reconstruct that tree. Actually the business of classification has today greater vitality and significance than ever before.

Nearly all the professional staff of the Museum of Natural History engage in systematic research of one form or another. In 1965, a focal point for these systematic interests, both within and outside the museum, was provided by the establishment within the museum of an Office of Systematics under the direction of Dr. Richard S. Cowan, who later became museum director. The principal functions of the office are to correlate the Institution's systematic studies, many of which are interdisciplinary, and to promote such major systematic projects as planning for a 15-year project on the flora of North America or developing a manual of Neotropical Squamata. The office supports and encourages field research as well as the longtime intramural studies of natural-history collections, arranges shared computer time, and engineers such chores as getting scientific papers translated and scientific illustrations prepared. In 1967, the office staged the first annual summer institute in systematics in collaboration with a number of outside agencies.

Another activity in which the Smithsonian has excelled, almost from its beginning, is its International Exchange Service, which has contributed to the diffusion of knowledge of inestimable magnitude.

In George B. Goode's *The Smithsonian Institution, 1846–1896*, Daniel C. Gilman remarked, "Correspondents were enlisted in every part of the United States, and great consideration was paid to their inquiries and suggestions." This kind of service to the public over the years has given the Smithsonian a reputation as a source of last resort on all manner of inquiry—historical, scientific, or technological, important or trivial—from professors, students, children, or those with unbridled curiosity. The Smithsonian tries to answer every letter received, and there have been untold thousands. In some cases, they can be answered by sending the inquirer a publication; others require hours of research on the part of a curator, clerk, or information officer. Often they are unintentionally amusing. I remember a letter from a schoolgirl in Southbury, Connecticut, in March, 1959, addressed to the Editorial and Publications Division:

Dear Sir:
I am writing to request any information on Franklin D. Roosevelt. I am doing a Term Paper on him in school. I will

appreciate any information you send me. I was unable to obtain enough information on my other term paper "The Horse and his Part in American History" so my teacher changed it to Franklin D. Roosevelt.

Another enduring contribution the Smithsonian has made to American science is the pattern, early established, of cooperation with all sorts of groups. Henry believed that the Smithsonian must not be isolationist but must extend its activities and influence beyond the scope directly covered by its limited income. Cooperation of some kind was absolutely necessary, for the Smithsonian simply did not have the funds or the staff to carry on all the activities it was called upon to perform, although it could always lend its prestige, correlate activities, and publish results. This reciprocity was healthy. It led to the Smithsonian's giving assistance to new ventures outside its walls, such as the U.S. Fish Commission, and working closely with others, such as the Geological Survey, the National Academy of Sciences, the American Philosophical Society, the American Association for the Advancement of Science, and with colleges and universities and individuals. The benefits to the Smithsonian from this kind of give and take have been vital in its life: the joint programs and projects have helped to establish the Smithsonian as the leading catalyst in American science and have given other institutions of learning and the scholarly world in general a feeling of proprietorship in the Institution.

Three other principal areas in which the Institution has made lasting contributions stand out. These are the Smithsonian's 3 A's: aeronautics, astrophysics, and anthropology. Each, from the beginning, has been of special concern.

The Institution's interest in aeronautics dates back to its pioneering meteorological research and studies on the nature of the atmosphere. In 1860, it was asked to aid Thaddeus Lowe in his efforts to cross the Atlantic by balloon, and the next year Secretary Henry took an active interest in Lowe's important balloon experiments in Washington. As early as 1863, Smithsonian annual reports included articles on aeronautical subjects, and Langley, of course, was the Smithsonian's greatest protagonist of aeronautics. The culmination of the tradition is seen today in the National Air and Space Museum, whose collections of historic aircraft and documentary material exceed in quantity and quality anything of their kind in the world.

Langley's pioneering in what he called the "new astronomy" led to the Institution's emphasis on astrophysics, which burgeoned into a full-fledged Smithsonian bureau, the Astrophysical Observatory. During its first half-century and more, under the leadership of Langley and Abbot, the observatory's research on solar radiations had far-reaching scientific importance. In recent years, it has contributed significantly to the nation's space program. Its publications have been voluminous and basic.

Finally, in all three branches of anthropology—archaeology, ethnology (including linguistics), and physical anthropology—the work of the Smithsonian has been notable. Again, from the very beginning, Henry gave anthropology high priority. His principal biographer, Thomas Coulson, stated that

> in his attitude toward archaeology and anthropology, Henry showed a liberalism that is noteworthy among scientists. The origin of the races of man, of man himself, of life and of species, the hypotheses of the anthropologists and archaeologists were matters which the laboratory scientists had too often regarded as incredulous, as not belonging to the true domain of science. Henry perceived the wisdom of applying the scientific method in these regions, and he showed his readiness to encourage anyone who embraced their investigation in the scientific spirit.

The Smithsonian became the foster parent of the new science of anthropology in America and gave it a home, drawing to it some of the world's most eminent men in the field. The flowering was in the Bureau of American Ethnology, whose name and nature became almost as renowned as that of the Smithsonian itself. Its architect and first director, John Wesley Powell, made the bureau a center of anthropological research in America and a clearinghouse for information pertaining to the American Indians. Although, three-quarters of a century after it was founded, the name and identity of this bureau were lost—a fact that seems to me to be one of the tragedies of American science—the present Secretary believes that the new Department of Anthropology "is emerging as a center of international anthropology through its organization of imaginative programs." It remains to be seen to what degree and in what ways this department's new research projects, developed by Smithsonian anthropologists and outside advisers, will make the Institution more a center of anthropology than it has always been.

For some time, plans have been gestating to centralize all the anthropological and related programs of the Institution into what will become another Smithsonian entity—the Center for the Study of Man. Dr. Sol Tax, a University of Chicago anthropologist, was brought in as a consultant to work out plans for its organization. The prospective program is broadly conceived and will serve not only the intramural needs of the Smithsonian's staff anthropologists but also the requirements of "scholars from outside whose interests lie in anthropology, archaeology, human ecology, and other fields concerned with appraising man's interrelationship with his physical, biological, and cultural environment." John Wesley Powell had a similar dream.

Looking Ahead

One of the most important activities of the Institution in recent years has been the successful attempt, particularly under the leadership of Secretary Carmichael, to obtain from

Congress the authorization for new Smithsonian buildings and funds for their erection—notably, the Museum of History and Technology, the two new wings for the Museum of Natural History, and the renovated Old Patent Office Building for two Smithsonian art galleries.

The large-scale museum exhibits construction and renovation program, which began in the 1950's and is still going on, has also been an outstanding achievement. It was accomplished not only through great financial expense to the government but also through a considerable sacrifice on the part of museum curators and others who had to shoulder the work of planning new exhibit halls, frequently at the expense of their research work. The result has been that no better exhibit halls can be seen anywhere in the world than in the Smithsonian's museums. Each hall is really a small museum in itself, and the educational potential for the millions who visit them is thrilling to consider.

But time marches on, and the Smithsonian has never remained static for very long. Its boast has always been that it must keep abreast of changing opportunities. Its circles are ever widening, and it is to be expected that some of its parts are occasionally sloughed off by sheer centrifugal force, perhaps aided by a shove now and then by impatient administrators.

A few of the new projects undertaken by the Smithsonian in the past five years represent not so much new activities as re-emphasis of old ideas, resurrection of latent potentials as new opportunities arise—in short, old wine in new bottles. One such is the emphasis today on education. The Smithsonian has always been pervasively an educational institution, but it was not until 1965 that the Office of Education and Training was created as an adjunct of the Secretariat. This office has attempted to correlate the educational work of the Institution in its more formal aspects; the job of its offshoot, the Office of Academic Programs, created in 1968, will be to make available the Smithsonian's collections and facilities for study and research in a wide range of scholarly subjects. Programs for higher education and research training are also projected, and in its first year the office awarded 138 fellowships and associateships to investigators conducting research in Smithsonian facilities.

In his 1968 annual report, the director of these programs, Dr. Philip C. Ritterbush, stated:

During this academic year the Smithsonian inaugurated a division of elementary and secondary education to draw upon collections, exhibits, audio-visual materials and other Smithsonian resources to augment and improve curricula for the nation's schools. . . . It has embarked upon a purposeful exploration of new kinds of educational experience for students at all levels of primary and secondary education.

The Smithsonian is also participating in community and social-action programs to provide increased employment and training opportunities for the physically handicapped, for young adults in need of summer employment, and for residents in the Washington metropolitan area desiring greater job opportunities.

Another new emphasis is in the field of oceanography. Although the Smithsonian has been concerned with this science for many decades, the increased attention being given it is reflected in the establishment of a coordinating Office of Oceanography and Limnology, set up in 1967. It reports directly to the assistant secretary for Science, and its work cuts across that of several other Smithsonian bureaus and offices. One of its prime activities is the Smithsonian Oceanographic Sorting Center, a signal service to all government oceanographic collecting.

Similarly, the science of ecology has now been elevated to "office" status, although ecology, in many other guises, has always been basic to much of the Smithsonian biological research. The emphasis today is on investigations dealing with animal population systems, vegetation, and whole ecosystems. The fitness of man's environment was the subject of an international symposium held at the Smithsonian in February, 1967. This new emphasis is a reflection of the general concern with the havoc that is being done to the earth's habitability. "Humanity is being jolted into a sharp awareness of its environment," wrote Dr. Helmut K. Buechner, head of the Smithsonian's new Office of Ecology, in a Smithsonian report. "We are entering a new era, scarcely imagined 25 years ago, in which society is facing the urgent need to adjust patterns of human culture to the physical and biological limitations of the earth's ecological patterns." Looking ahead, Smithsonian ecologists believe that there will be, during the next five years particularly, "unprecedented opportunities for ecological research and international conservation efforts."

Though many individuals associated with the Smithsonian have been ardent conservationists, the Institution itself has perhaps wisely steered clear of the controversies that the conservation of natural resources engenders. Two of the Smithsonian's early mentors, Baird and Powell, were both conservationists before the term was applied to natural resources, but they did not leave a truly conservationist imprint on the Smithsonian, perhaps because it was an activity that other branches of the government were involved in. Secretary Ripley, however, has brought conservation into the Smithsonian's orbit of concerns, and the Institution is already participating in an International Biological Program, among whose objectives are the establishment of a world network of nature reserves and the development of a world program in conservation. "It is highly important," stated Ripley, in *National Parks Magazine* in 1966,

that ecological bench marks be set aside for scientific research.

Some of these may be national parks, others wilderness areas, and still others small nature reserves. They should not be merely set aside for posterity—they should be carefully studied for their contributions to knowledge now and in the future. One of the Smithsonian's major contributions to this network of reserves can be in the inventories of the biological components and general descriptions of the ecosystems preserved. This will require increased personnel, space, and facilities.

That museums are important elements of the cultural and educational development of the United States is a conclusion not difficult to arrive at when it is realized that the annual attendance at U.S. museums is well over 300 million. The National Museum Act, signed by President Johnson in October, 1966, reaffirmed the Smithsonian's role of assisting museums and authorized appropriations to meet needs and to study problems common to all museums. In his 1967 annual report, Secretary Ripley commented: "Though no appropriations have been made under the Act, it has stimulated requests for aid from every State and a score of nations." The Smithsonian's director general of museums, Frank A. Taylor, is responsible for carrying out the Act, which provides the legislative framework for programs of museum training, research, conservation, surveys, and publications. It is another instance of the broadening of Smithsonian horizons, but the keynote remains cooperation, an old forte of the Institution.

In general, it can be said that the Smithsonian administrators during the past five years have re-endorsed the traditional role of the Institution in research and education but at the same time have projected this role wherever possible to the vital problems of today. They are realizing increasingly that the Smithsonian cannot afford to retain whatever image it may have had of ivory-towerism. They believe it must continually project itself, even at the expense of costly mistakes and experiments. As one expression of this, Secretary Ripley wrote in his 1967 annual report:

What is there that we at the Smithsonian can think upon which would illumine the basic problems confronting social biology? There are certainly three paths along which we might travel toward illumination: one leads to the study of terrestrial environment, another to the study of social environment, and the third to the study of man as an evolving species.

Many of the Smithsonian's recent new directions can be seen to follow these paths. They are aimed toward a more deliberate philosophy of Smithsonian action. Of course, there is a certain danger that, because the Institution has something less than financial independence and often does not know whether next year's government support will be forthcoming, it will bite off more than it can chew and be diverted from the lines it has drawn for itself. But this is a chance it has always taken and must continue to take.

There is a danger, too, that the Smithsonian will create a bifocal image and that this image will become somewhat blurred in the mind of the public. On the one hand, it is attempting to preserve the reputation of the Smithsonian as a leading research organization—the dream of Joseph Henry and all his successors—and to identify itself more closely with the academic world by offering programs in higher education and research training, fellowships, and similar opportunities. On the other hand, it is investing its activities with a good deal of showmanship that draws larger and larger crowds to its programs on the Mall in Washington and to its museum halls and special events. Perhaps the Smithsonian can be all things to all people, but there are some who hope that it will never truly merit the sobriquet already given it by Geoffrey Hellman—"octopus on the Mall."

One of the results of the recent avidity of the Smithsonian to take on new jobs, to take up new lines of research, or to reactivate old ones has been a breakdown to some degree in its compartments of organization. Some of the new offices created seem to defy the logic of traditional organization and make an organization chart look as if a hurricane had struck it. Organizational development is not a straight line but a circle, whereon centralization follows on the heels of decentralization and vice versa. As far back as 1897, for example, the National Museum was reorganized and the various divisions gathered up into three departments with three scientists in charge as head curators. This was an effort toward centralization. But gradually modification set in, brought about usually when a division expanded and demanded an identity of its own. For example, first the museum's department of biology broke down into two departments, zoology and botany, and later the division of entomology broke away to become a full department itself.

Another instance of this decentralization-centralization-decentralization evolution occurred in the Institution's editorial activities. Prior to 1931, each Smithsonian bureau operated pretty much independently editorially. In that year, the editorial work was centralized into the Editorial Division, with what appeared to be increased efficiency. In the early 1960's, however, the Institution's individual divisions, departments, and bureaus—and by this time there were many more of them—began to clamor to be freed of central editorial control, and the director of the Smithsonian Institution Press, as the editorial unit became known in 1966, found it easier to yield to decentralization than to fight it. The process is likely to continue until it again gets out of hand and the whole function is again centralized.

Some of the more recently created offices—the Office of Ecology, the Office of Oceanography and Limnology, the Office of Education and Training, and the Office of Academic Programs—have found no home within the existing traditional framework. Whereas a few years ago the organization chart of the Smithsonian was a relatively simple affair, today it reflects an attempt to organize activities along functional rather than "bureaucratic" lines. There is evident a certain groping for a settled organization, an exercise in wishful, but withal undoubtedly healthy, thinking.

An internal criticism one hears today is that the Smithsonian is becoming top-heavy with administrators, that the "palace guard" is getting out of hand, a situation that does not contribute to salutary morale. But it is bound to happen as an organization grows bigger. "With bigness," said E. B. White, "comes remoteness, inaccessibility. This is bad, and it causes trouble."

The secret is in motivation and willingness to grow without making a fetish of bigness. The motivation is inherent in James Smithson's prescription—increase and diffusion. The willingness has never been lacking. Every Secretary from Joseph Henry on has re-examined Smithson's principles for himself and in his own way has interpreted them toward a renewal of "the Institution's zeal in the increase of the sum total of man's knowledge."

"The Institution should continue to strive toward the end that man should not only know better his earthly abode, but should acquire the means of knowing himself better. Such studies are of vital significance in our present efforts to build a better world order, and to break the cycle of recurring wars of ever-increasing destructiveness." This statement was made by President Harry S. Truman on August 10, 1946, in a press release issued from the White House in observance of the Smithsonian's founding. It could have been written yesterday. It is but another expression of the open-endedness that has given the Institution its perennial vitality.

Appendix A

Career Opportunities
at the Smithsonian

To perform the work of the Smithsonian Institution requires a vast array of qualified people, probably as diversified in their qualifications and skills as any to be found elsewhere in government. In research, there are anthropologists, zoologists, botanists, geologists, physicists, astronomers, taxonomists, oceanographers, ecologists. In museum administration, there are curators, laboratory technicians, taxidermists, exhibits specialists, electricians, plumbers, painters, carpenters, guards, animal keepers. In services, there are writers and editors, photographers, artists, lawyers, publicity experts, librarians. And, of course, there is the usual complement of executives, administrative assistants, stenographers, typists, clerks, personnel officers, and others. Altogether, the opportunities for employment at the Smithsonian are considerable, although the total number of persons employed by the Institution—about three thousand in 1968—is not large in comparison with that of most government agencies.

RECRUITMENT AND HIRING

The fiscal dichotomy under which the Institution operates governs the recruiting and hiring of personnel. Employees whose salaries are paid from government appropriations must in most instances qualify in civil service examinations. When hired, they become a part of the federal civil service system and are entitled to retirement benefits and other fringe advantages of that system. Employees

233

whose salaries are paid from private Smithsonian funds are not under civil service jurisdiction. For these private employees, however, the Institution has adopted a general policy of requiring qualifications comparable to those for the civil service. The salary levels, requirements for promotions, standards of performance, incentive awards, and annual and sick leave benefits are identical. The only difference lies in a greater flexibility in recruiting, hiring, and firing in the case of the private employees. Occasionally, a person hired under civil service is transferred to the private rolls, and this can be done easily if the employee agrees to relinquish his civil service status. It is not easy, however, to transfer a Smithsonian employee from private rolls to civil service rolls, for he must first obtain civil service status, usually by taking an examination and then competing with others who have qualified in that particular category of position. This process is sometimes laborious and frustrating.

SALARIES

Smithsonian salaries are maintained at the federal government level. At the present time, for example, a clerk-typist (GS-4) may be paid an annual salary of $5,522 to $7,178; a stenographer (GS-7), $7,639 to $9,934; an administrative assistant (GS-11), $11,233 to $14,599; a curator (GS-12), $13,389 to $17,403; a research scientist (GS-14), $18,531 to $24,093; a department head (GS-17), $28,976 to $32,840. The table on page 235 gives the salary ranges as of July 13, 1969.

Opportunities for employment at the Smithsonian are limited quantitatively but not qualitatively. Many of its positions are highly specialized and therefore are difficult to fill. For many positions on the professional staff, the Institution finds itself in competition with universities and industry, which are constantly searching for talented young personnel trained in the sciences and the technologies. Although the government maintains a general policy that federal salary rates shall be comparable with private-enterprise rates for the same levels of work, industry always seems to be one

Smithsonian Institution: Per annum rates and steps effective July 13, 1969

(GS)	1	2	3	4	5	6	7	8	9	10
1	$3,889	$4,019	$4,149	$4,279	$4,408	$4,538	$4,668	$4,798	$4,928	$5,057
2	4,360	4,505	4,650	4,795	4,940	5,085	5,230	5,375	5,520	5,665
3	4,917	5,081	5,245	5,409	5,573	5,737	5,901	6,065	6,229	6,393
4	5,522	5,706	5,890	6,074	6,258	6,442	6,626	6,810	6,994	7,178
5	6,176	6,382	6,588	6,794	7,000	7,206	7,412	7,618	7,824	8,030
6	6,882	7,111	7,340	7,569	7,798	8,027	8,256	8,485	8,714	8,943
7	7,639	7,894	8,149	8,404	8,659	8,914	9,169	9,424	9,679	9,934
8	8,449	8,731	9,013	9,295	9,577	9,859	10,141	10,423	10,705	10,987
9	9,320	9,631	9,942	10,253	10,564	10,875	11,186	11,497	11,808	12,119
10	10,252	10,594	10,936	11,278	11,620	11,962	12,304	12,646	12,988	13,330
11	11,233	11,607	11,981	12,355	12,729	13,103	13,477	13,851	14,225	14,599
12	13,389	13,835	14,281	14,727	15,173	15,619	16,065	16,511	16,957	17,403
13	15,812	16,339	16,866	17,393	17,920	18,447	18,974	19,501	20,028	20,555
14	18,531	19,149	19,767	20,385	21,003	21,621	22,239	22,857	23,475	24,093
15	21,589	22,309	23,029	23,749	24,469	25,189	25,909	26,629	27,349	28,069
16	25,044	25,879	26,714	27,549	28,384	29,219	30,054	30,889	31,724	—
17	28,976	29,942	30,908	31,874	32,840	—	—	—	—	—
18	33,495	—	—	—	—	—	—	—	—	—

jump ahead and able to grab a good many of the best people. Some academically trained persons, too, after a few years in the government, begin to hanker again for the academic life and return to colleges or accept attractive offers from private research organizations.

ACADEMIC REQUIREMENTS

Academic requirements for the top scientific positions at the Smithsonian are relatively high. Curators, who in most instances also carry on research, must have a Ph.D. in the appropriate subject-matter area. Employees in the research and curatorial fields who may not have their doctorates are encouraged to get them and to take advantage of job-training opportunities.

Under a 1958 law, federal agencies are even authorized to pay employees' tuition at colleges, universities, professional institutes, industrial laboratories, or research foundations, all in the interests of obtaining and holding the best-qualified personnel in federal service. There are long-range programs designed to attract quality personnel to full-time federal employment upon attainment of their degrees. A program is usually arranged so that the student alternates about six months of academic training at an accredited college or university with an equal period of work experience in a government agency.

CAREER SECURITY

Career security at the Smithsonian, as elsewhere in government service, is perennially threatened by the uncertainties of the federal economy. Affluent years are most certainly to be followed by lean years, and administrators must not be too optimistic in their ability to project and to staff programs for the future. In the summer of 1968, for example, Congress directed that all government agencies cut back their employment figures to the June, 1966, level. The effect of this cutback order on the Smithsonian was felt to be unusually serious in the face of the Institution's recent efforts to increase its services to the public. Secretary Ripley, in an article in *The Torch,* pointed out that the directive threatened both the morale of the staff and the Smithsonian's national responsibilities. He said:

The Institution stands to lose 234 more employees at a time when the guard and maintenance forces are already below par and new museums require staffing. This would bring about serious shortages in buildings management personnel, cause more expense for overtime pay, and largely defer preventive maintenance to a physical plant valued at $170 million. The Institution, in effect, would be hard put to protect an investment of more than $10 million, which has gone into more than 1,000 exhibits since 1964.

A substantial closing of public exhibits becomes a real likelihood if the current minimal level of protection cannot be maintained. A survey has been conducted of the required number of guard posts which should be manned for adequate protection of visitors to our museums and art galleries and against vandalism of the national collections and the buildings. It revealed that only 85 per cent of the essential posts can be staffed with current manpower, as compared with 96 per cent in fiscal 1965. This is before further cutbacks by the Revenue and Expenditure Control Act of 1968 are felt.

The number of instances of vandalism has increased from 47 incidents in calendar year 1965 to 183 in 1967. There have been 194 incidents since January of this year. We can foresee a major impairment in our ability to maintain and protect our buildings and collections—some 60 million specimens in science, history, and art—and to serve the public.

Cutbacks in the already hard-pressed exhibits staff will result in a steady deterioration of public loss of a major public investment.

No less than one-third of our staff members are directly concerned with serving the public in daily face-to-face communication with visitors to our buildings and with researchers who come for extended stays to use the collections for serious studies.

An employee coming to the Smithsonian for the first time should realize some of the uncertainties of government service—particularly that it is not always the employer's fault if prospects held out for advancement, promotions, tenure, and continuity of programs cannot be fulfilled. With all the advantages of public service, there are certain conditions inherent in the government system that no one can do much about.

The Great Challenge

Over the years, the aura of intellectual freedom that has characterized the Smithsonian has made it an attractive place in which to work and has engendered a salubrious loyalty on the part of most of its employees. One of the expressed goals of the Office of Personnel is "to create a climate which encourages individual expression, releases creativity, ignites imagination, and fosters hope, trust, openness, and meaningful cooperation"—a large order indeed. By and large, however, once an employee gets established in the Institution, he hates to leave, and many a scientist, after he has officially been retired, elects to continue at the Institution if he is provided an office cubbyhole in which to hang his hat and quietly carry on his work, without salary, of course. Many are given emeritus or associate status. Mrs. Agnes Chase, for example, a world-renowned agrostologist, continued her botanical research at the National Herbarium for more than twenty years after she retired, and her work was terminated only by her death at the age of ninety-four. Dr. Waldo L. Schmitt began working as a young zoologist at the National Museum in 1910; he retired in 1957 at the age of seventy but has been coming to his laboratory to continue his work on the collections of Crustacea ever since.

In writing of his days at the Smithsonian, first as librarian and later as an assistant secretary, Dr. Cyrus Adler caught something of the Smithsonian atmosphere that prevailed at the turn of the century:

> Here, then, began a period . . . of my life which flowed on busily, interestingly, with many problems and questions and even excitements, but no worries. . . . We all believed the world was getting better and better. We were satisfied that science and learning were making steady progress toward an end which would surely attain, if not perfection, at least great improvement in the state of the individual and society. . . . In other words, the time was ripe . . . for pure intellectual and aesthetic enjoyment of life; and for the next fifteen years I had this, in what I deemed the most pleasurable surroundings one could find in these United States.

One will not find today much of this utopian smugness among Smithsonian people; the world has changed and there are plenty of worries. But there still linger, though to a lesser extent than formerly, the pleasurable surroundings of an intellectual environment that appeal to the Smithsonian community of scholars.

Today, the Smithsonian holds out to the prospective employee unique opportunities, particularly in research and in museum administration and education. It stresses these opportunities in a booklet, rather widely distributed to the academic world, entitled *Smithsonian Research Opportunities,* which has been published annually since 1964. The booklet describes Smithsonian study and research facilities under ten categories reflecting academic disciplines—American studies, history of science and technology, history of art, anthropology and cultural studies, physical sciences, environmental biology, evolutionary and systematic biology, evolutionary biology (tropical zones), information and reference systems, and museum studies. It aims to attract not only those who eventually might aspire to careers at the Institution but also those who wish to take advantage of its academic programs for research associates, post- and predoctoral associates, and others. It emphasizes the freedom of the Institution's research pursuits. "The most distinctive quality of Smithsonian research," the booklet states,

arises from participation in a common enterprise which fosters a cooperative spirit and frequent consultation, without undue supervision or any sacrifice of individual independence to superimposed objectives. The cooperative work and individual effort that have been customary in Smithsonian research arise from the individual investigator's perception of common objectives within the framework of a single institution. They will continue to be, as they have been, a matter for individual choice in response to opportunity.

Appendix B

Selected Smithsonian Publications

To choose a representative list from among the several thousand Smithsonian publications issued during the Institution's 120 years of publishing history is not an easy task, especially for one who spent the larger part of his career in the Institution's Editorial and Publications Division. Another compiler surely might come up with a somewhat, if not totally, different result. Such a list, though it may reflect some arbitrary choices, is useful in indicating the nature, scope, diversity in subject matter and authorship, and quality of the publication output. In general, the approximately 100 works here selected are those that are monographic in character, that have attained some reputation and importance as the years have passed, and that may be regarded as typical specimens of the Institution's program.

The persons responsible for deciding what the Institution publishes have in the main endeavored to serve the needs of the basic sciences and arts rather than popular demand. Commercial publishers can seldom afford to publish books that they know will not pay, with the result that many books that might add to the sum total of man's knowledge must either be subsidized or remain unpublished. The Institution has been a generous subsidizer and thus has brought out many basic works of limited distribution that otherwise never would have appeared in print. It is this policy that has given the Smithsonian's publishing record distinction. If the Smithsonian has ever published a best seller, it has been largely by accident. The principal aim of the program has been to diffuse knowledge at all levels, and this objective is still a good one to strive for.

KEY TO ABBREVIATIONS

Annual Report of the Bureau of American Ethnology	Ann. Rep. Bur. Amer. Ethnol.
Annual Report of the United States National Musem	Ann. Rep. U.S. Nat. Mus.
Annual Report of the Smithsonian Institution	Smithsonian Ann. Rep.
Bureau of American Ethnology Bulletin	Bur. Amer. Ethnol. Bull.
Contributions from the United States National Herbarium	Contr. U.S. Nat. Herb.
Publications of the Institute of Social Anthropology	Inst. Soc. Anthrop. Publ.
Proceedings of the United States National Museum	Proc. U.S. Nat. Mus.
Smithsonian Contributions to Knowledge	Smithsonian Contr. Knowl.
Smithsonian Miscellaneous Collections	Smithsonian Misc. Coll.
Smithsonian Special Publication	Smithsonian Spec. Publ.
United States National Museum Bulletin	U.S. Nat. Mus. Bull.

ABBOT, CHARLES GREELEY. 1960. *A Long-range Forecast of United States Precipitation.* Smithsonian Misc. Coll., vol. 139, no. 9. 78 pp., illus.

ADNEY, EDWIN TAPPAN, AND CHAPELLE, HOWARD I. 1964. *The Bark and Skin Boats of North America.* U.S. Nat. Mus. Bull. 230. 242 pp., illus.

AGASSIZ, LOUIS. 1850. *The Classification of Insects from Embryological Data.* Smithsonian Contr. Knowl., vol. 2, no. 16. 28 pp., illus.

ALBATROSS EXPEDITION. 1917–43. *Contributions to the Biology of the Philippine Archipelago and Adjacent Regions.* U.S. Nat. Mus. Bull. 100. In several vols., illus.

BAIRD, SPENCER FULLERTON. 1864–66. *Review of North American Birds in the Museum of the Smithsonian Institution.* Smithsonian Misc. Coll., vol. 12. 484 pp., illus.

BENT, ARTHUR CLEVELAND, AND COLLABORATORS. 1919–68. *Life Histories of North American Birds.* U.S. National Museum Bull., 21 vols., illus.

BOAS, FRANZ. 1911, 1917. *Handbook of the American Indian Languages.* Bur. Amer. Ethnol. Bull. 40. pt. I, 1,069 pp.; pt. II, 903 pp.

BOLTON, H. CARRINGTON. 1893. *A Select Bibliography of Chemistry, 1492–1892.* Smithsonian Misc. Coll., vol. 41. 1,225 pp. Supplements issued in 1899 and 1904.

BROCKETT, PAUL. 1910. *Bibliography of Aeronautics.* Smithsonian Misc. Coll., vol. 55. 940 pp.

CHASE, AGNES. 1959. *First Book of Grasses.* 3d ed. Smithsonian Spec. Publ., no. 4351. 127 pp., illus.

CLARK, AUSTIN HOBART. 1915–67. *A Monograph of the Existing Crinoids.* U.S. Nat. Mus. Bull. 82, vol. 1. 5 pts., illus.

CLARK, AUSTIN HOBART, AND CLARK, LEILA FORBES. 1951. *The Butterflies of Virginia.* Smithsonian Misc. Coll., vol. 116, no. 7. 239 pp., illus.

CLARKE, FRANK WIGGLESWORTH. 1873. *The Constants of Nature.* Smithsonian Misc. Coll., vol. 12. 272 pp.

CLAYTON, HENRY HELM. 1927. *World Weather Records.* Smithsonian Misc. Coll., vol. 79. 1,199 pp.

COFFIN, JAMES HENRY. 1875. *The Winds of the Globe.* Smithsonian Contr. Knowl., vol. 20. 781 pp., illus.

COLLINS, HENRY BASCOM. 1937. *Archeology of St. Lawrence Island, Alaska.* Smithsonian Misc. Coll., vol. 96, no. 1. 431 pp., illus.

COOPER, GUSTAV ARTHUR. 1956. *Chazyan and Related Brachiopods.* Smithsonian Misc. Coll., vol. 127. pt. I, 1,024 pp.; pt. II, plates.

COOPER, JAMES GRAHAM. 1859. *On the Distribution of the Forests and Trees of North America, With Notes on its Physical Geography.* Smithsonian Spec. Publ., no. 351. 36 pp.

CULIN, STEWART. 1907. "Games of the North American Indians." *Ann. Rep. Bur. Amer. Ethnol.,* 1902–03, pp. 3–809, illus.

CUSHMAN, JOSEPH AUGUSTINE. 1910–17. *A Monograph of the Foraminifera of the North Pacific Ocean.* U.S. Nat. Mus. Bull. 71. 6 pts., illus.

DALMAT, HERBERT T. 1955. *The Black Flies of Guatemala and Their Role as Vectors of Onchocerciasis.* Smithsonian Misc. Coll., vol. 125, no. 1. 425 pp., illus.

DONALDSON, THOMAS. 1887. "The George Catlin Indian Gallery." *Ann. Rep. U.S. Nat. Mus.,* 1885, pt. 5. 939 pp., illus.

EDITORIAL DIVISION, SMITHSONIAN INSTITUTION. 1947. *A List and Index of the Publications of the United States National Museum, 1875–1946.* U.S. Nat. Mus. Bull. 193. 306 pp.

EWERS, JOHN C. 1955. *The Horse in Blackfoot Culture.* Bur. Amer. Ethnol. Bull. 159. 374 pp., illus.

GODDARD, ROBERT H. 1919. *A Method of Reaching Extreme Altitudes.* Smithsonian Misc. Coll., vol. 71, no. 2. 69 pp., illus.

GOLDMAN, EDWARD ALPHONSO. 1920. *Mammals of Panama.* Smithsonian Misc. Coll., vol. 69, no. 1. 309 pp., illus.

GOODE, GEORGE BROWN. 1901. *A Memorial to George Brown Goode,*

Together with a Selection of his Papers on Museums and on the History of Science in America. Ann. Rep. U.S. Nat. Mus., vol. 2, 1897. 515 pp., illus.

GOODE, GEORGE BROWN, AND BEAN, TARLETON HOFFMAN. 1895. *Oceanic Ichthyology.* U.S. Nat. Mus. Spec. Bull. 2. vol. 1, 553 pp.; vol. II, 26 pp., illus.

GOULD, BENJAMIN A. 1850. *Report on the History of the Discovery of Neptune.* Smithsonian Spec. Publ., no. 18. 56 pp.

GUYOT, ARNOLD. 1852. A Collection of Meteorological Tables, with Other Tables Useful in Practical Meteorology. 212 pp. (This collection was the forerunner of several volumes of Smithsonian tables in meteorology, mathematics, physics, and geography, some of which are still in print.)

HALE, MASON E., JR. 1961. *Lichen Handbook.* Smithsonian Spec. Publ., no. 4434. 178 pp., illus.

HENRY, JOSEPH. 1857. "On the Mode of Testing Building Materials, and an Account of the Marble Used in the Extension of the United States Capitol." *Smithsonian Ann. Rep.,* 1856, pp. 303–310.

————. 1886. *The Scientific Writings of Joseph Henry.* Smithsonian Misc. Coll., vol. 30.

HERBER, ELMER CHARLES, ed. 1963. *Correspondence Between Spencer Fullerton Baird and Louis Agassiz, Two Pioneer American Naturalists.* Smithsonian Spec. Publ., no. 4515. 237 pp., illus.

HITCHCOCK, ALBERT S., AND STANDLEY, PAUL C. 1919. *Flora of the District of Columbia and Vicinity.* Contr. U.S. Nat. Herb., vol. 21. 329 pp., illus.

HITCHCOCK, EDWARD. 1857. *Illustrations of Surface Geology.* Smithsonian Contr. Knowl., vol. 9. 164 pp., illus.

HODGE, FREDERICK WEBB, ed. 1907, 1910. *Handbook of American Indians North of Mexico.* Bur. Amer. Ethnol. Bull. 30. vol. I, 972 pp.; vol. II, 1,221 pp., illus.

HODGE, PAUL W., AND WRIGHT, FRANCES W. 1967. *The Large Magellanic Cloud.* Smithsonian Spec. Publ., no. 4699. 108 pp., illus.

HOLMES, WILLIAM HENRY. 1919. *Handbook of Aboriginal American Antiquities: The Lithic Industries.* Bur. Amer. Ethnol. Bull. 60. 380 pp., illus.

HORNADAY, WILLIAM TEMPLE. 1889. "The Extinction of the American Bison." *Ann. Rep. U.S. Nat. Mus.,* 1886–87, pp. 369–548, illus.

HOUGH, WALTER. 1926. *Fire as an Agent in Human Culture.* U.S. Nat. Mus. Bull. 139. 270 pp., illus.

HOWARD, LELAND OSSIAN. 1930. *A History of Applied Entomology.* Smithsonian Misc. Coll., vol. 84. 564 pp., illus.

HRDLIČKA, ALEŠ. 1930. *The Skeletal Remains of Early Man.* Smithsonian Misc. Coll., vol. 83. 379 pp., illus.

JEWETT, CHARLES COFFIN. 1852. *On the Construction of Catalogues of Libraries, and Their Publication by Means of Separate Stereotype Titles, with Rules and Examples.* Smithsonian Spec. Publ., no. 47. 78 pp. Reissued in 1853.

JORDAN, DAVID STARR. 1896–1900. *The Fishes of North and Middle America.* U.S. Nat. Mus. Bull. 47. 4 pts. 3,313 pp., 392 pls.

JUDD, NEIL MERTON. 1954. *Material Culture of Pueblo Bonito.* Smithsonian Misc. Coll., vol. 124. 398 pp., illus.

―――. 1959. *Pueblo del Arroyo, Chaco Canyon, New Mexico.* Smithsonian Misc. Coll., vol. 138. 222 pp., illus.

―――. 1964. *The Architecture of Pueblo Bonito.* Smithsonian Misc. Coll., vol. 147. 349 pp., illus.

KAINEN, JACOB. 1962. *John Baptist Jackson: 18th-Century Master of the Color Woodcut,* U.S. Nat. Mus. Bull. 222. 183 pp., illus.

KROEBER, A. L. 1925. *Handbook of the Indians of California.* Bur. Amer. Ethnol. Bull. 78. 995 pp., illus.

LANGLEY, SAMUEL P., AND MANLY, CHARLES M. 1911. *Langley Memoir on Mechanical Flight.* Smithsonian Contr. Knowl., vol. 27, no. 3. 320 pp., illus.

LEIDY, JOSEPH. 1865. *Cretaceous Reptiles of the United States.* Smithsonian Contr. Knowl., vol. 14. 142 pp., illus.

LEWIS, BERKELEY R. 1956. *Small Arms and Ammunition in the United States Service, 1776–1865.* Smithsonian Misc. Coll., vol. 129. 338 pp., illus.

MALLERY, GARRICK. 1894. "Picture-Writing of the American Indians." *Ann. Rep. Bur. Amer. Ethnol.,* 1889–90. 807 pp.

MASON, OTIS TUFTON. 1904. "Aboriginal American Basketry." *Ann. Rep. U.S. Nat. Mus.,* 1902, pp. 171–548, illus.

MEARNS, EDGAR ALEXANDER. 1907. *Mammals of the Mexican Boundary of the United States.* U.S. Nat. Mus. Bull. 56. 530 pp., illus.

MEGGERS, BETTY J., AND EVANS, CLIFFORD, eds. 1963. *Aboriginal Cultural Development in Latin America: An Interpretative Review.* Smithsonian Misc. Coll., vol. 148, no. 1. 148 pp., illus.

MERRILL, GEORGE PERKINS. 1906. "Contributions to the History of American Geology." *Ann. Rep. U.S. Nat. Mus.,* 1904, pp. 189–733, illus.

MILLER, GERRIT SMITH, JR., AND KELLOGG, REMINGTON. 1955. *List of North American Recent Mammals.* U.S. Nat. Mus. Bull. 205. 954 pp.

MOONEY, JAMES. 1900. "Myths of the Cherokee." *Ann. Rep. Bur. Amer. Ethnol.,* 1897–98, pp. 3–548.

MORGAN, LEWIS HENRY. 1869. *Systems of Consanguinity and Affinity of the Human Family.* Smithsonian Contr. Knowl., vol. 17, 616 pp., illus.

MORLEY, EDWARD WILLIAMS. 1895. *On the Densities of Oxygen and*

Hydrogen, and the Ratio of Their Atomic Weights. Smithsonian Contr. Knowl., vol. 29, no. 2. 117 pp.

MORLEY, SYLVANUS G. 1915. *An Introduction to the Study of the Maya Hieroglyphs.* Bur. Amer. Ethnol. Bull. 57. 284 pp., illus.

MUIR, JOHN. 1902. *Notes on the Pacific Coast Glaciers.* Harriman Alaska Series, vol. 1. pp. 119–135. illus.

NELSON, EDWARD WILLIAM. 1899. "The Eskimo About Bering Strait." *Ann. Rep. Bur. Amer. Ethnol.,* 1896–97, pp. 3–518, illus.

OHWI, JISABURO. 1965. *Flora of Japan.* Edited by Frederick G. Meyer and Egbert H. Walker. Smithsonian Spec. Publ., no. 4542. 1,067 pp., illus.

PARSONS, ELSIE CLEWS. 1962. *Isleta Paintings.* Edited by Esther S. Goldfrank. Bur. Amer. Ethnol. Bull. 181. 299 pp., 140 pls.

PERRY, STUART H. 1944. *The Metallography of Meteoric Iron.* U.S. Nat. Mus. Bull. 184. 206 pp., illus.

POPE, J. A., *et al.* 1967. *The Freer Chinese Bronzes.* Freer Gallery of Art Oriental Studies, no. 7. 638 pp., 116 pls.

POPE, JOHN ALEXANDER. 1956. *Chinese Porcelains of the Ardebil Shrine.* Freer Gallery of Art. 194 pp., 142 pls.

POWELL, JOHN WESLEY. 1891. "Indian Linguistic Families of America, North of Mexico." *Ann. Rep. Bur. Amer. Ethnol.,* 1885–86. 142 pp., map.

PUMPELLY, RAPHAEL. 1866. *Geological Researches in China, Mongolia, and Japan During the Years 1862 to 1865.* Smithsonian Contr. Knowl., vol. 15. 173 pp., illus.

RATHBUN, MARY JANE. 1937. *The Oxystomatous and Allied Crabs of America.* U.S. Nat. Mus. Bull. 166. 278 pp., illus.

RIDGWAY, ROBERT. 1892. "The Humming Birds." *U.S. Nat. Mus. Ann. Rep.,* 1890, pp. 253–383, illus.

RIDGWAY, ROBERT, AND FRIEDMANN, HERBERT. 1901–46. *The Birds of North and Middle America.* U.S. Nat. Mus. Bull. 50. 10 vols.

ROCKHILL, WILLIAM WOODVILLE. 1894. *Diary of a Journey Through Mongolia and Tibet in 1891 and 1892.* 413 pp., illus.

SCUDDER, SAMUEL H. 1882. *Nomenclator Zoologicus: An Alphabetical List of All Generic Names That Have Been Employed by Naturalists for Recent and Fossil Animals from the Earliest Times to the Close of the Year 1879.* U.S. Nat. Mus. Bull. 19. 398 pp.

SHALER, NATHANIEL SOUTHGATE. 1903. *A Comparison of the Features of the Earth and the Moon.* Smithsonian Contr. Knowl., vol. 34. 130 pp., illus.

SMITH, LYMAN B. 1955. *The Bromeliaceae of Brazil.* Smithsonian Misc. Coll., vol. 126, no. 1. 290 pp., illus.

SMITHSONIAN INSTITUTION. 1940. *Essays in Historical Anthropology of North America: Published in Honor of John R. Swanton in*

Celebration of His 40th Year with the Smithsonian Institution. Smithsonian Misc. Coll., vol. 100. 600 pp., illus.

―――. 1959. *Studies in Invertebrate Morphology: Published in Honor of Dr. Robert Evans Snodgrass on the Occasion of His 84th Birthday, July 15, 1959.* Smithsonian Misc. Coll., vol. 137. 416 pp., illus.

SMITHSONIAN TRAVELING EXHIBITION SERVICE. 1965. *Dürer and His Time.* 252 pp., 150 pls.

SNYDER, THOMAS ELIOT. 1949. *Catalog of the Termites (Isoptera) of the World.* Smithsonian Misc. Coll., vol. 112. 490 pp.

SQUIER, E. G., AND DAVIS, E. H. 1848. *Ancient Monuments of the Mississippi Valley.* Smithsonian Contr. Knowl., vol. 1. 346 pp., illus.

STANDLEY, PAUL C. 1920–26. *Trees and Shrubs of Mexico.* Contr. U.S. Nat. Herb., vol. 23. 5 pts. and index, 1,721 pp.

STEJNEGER, LEONHARD. 1907. *Herpetology of Japan and Adjacent Territory.* U.S. Nat. Mus. Bull. 58. 577 pp., illus.

STEMPLE, RUTH M., AND EDITORIAL AND PUBLICATIONS DIVISION, comp. 1963. *Author-Subject Index to Articles in Smithsonian Annual Reports, 1849–1961.* Smithsonian Spec. Publ., no. 4503. 200 pp.

STEWARD, JULIAN H., ed., 1946–59. *Handbook of South American Indians.* Bur. Amer. Ethnol. Bull. 143. vol. I, 624 pp.; vol. II, 1,035 pp.; vol. III, 986 pp.; vol. IV, 609 pp.; vol. V, 818 pp.; vol. VI, 715 pp.; vol. VII, 286 pp., illus.

STIRLING, MATTHEW W. 1943. *The Native Peoples of New Guinea.* War Background Series no. 9. 25 pp., illus.

SWANTON, JOHN REED. 1952. *The Indian Tribes of North America.* Bur. Amer. Ethnol. Bull. 145. 726 pp., maps.

TAX, SOL. 1953. *Penny Capitalism: A Guatemalan Indian Economy.* Inst. Soc. Anthrop. Publ. 16. 230 pp., illus.

THOMPSON, ERNEST E. [SETON, ERNEST THOMPSON]. 1891. "The Birds of Manitoba." *Proc. U.S. Nat. Mus.,* vol. 13, pp. 457–643.

TRUE, FREDERICK W. 1910. *An Account of the Beaked Whales of the Family Ziphiidae.* U.S. Nat. Mus. Bull. 73. 89 pp., illus.

VÁZQUEZ DE ESPINOSA, ANTONIO. 1942. *Compendium and Description of the West Indies.* Translated by Charles Upson Clark. Smithsonian Misc. Coll., vol. 102. 862 pp.

WALCOTT, CHARLES DOOLITTLE. 1908. *Cambrian Trilobites.* Smithsonian Misc. Coll., vol. 53, pp. 13–52, illus.

WALCOTT, MARY VAUX. 1925. *North American Wild Flowers.* 5 portfolio vols., 400 pls.

WEDEL, WALDO R. 1959. *An Introduction to Kansas Archeology.* Bur. Amer. Ethnol. Bull. 174. 723 pp., illus.

WETMORE, ALEXANDER. 1960. *A Classification for the Birds of the World.* Smithsonian Misc. Coll., vol. 139, no. 11. 37 pp.

———. 1965, 1968. *The Birds of the Republic of Panama.* vol. I, 483 pp.; vol. II, 605 pp., illus.

WILLEY, GORDON R. 1949. *Archeology of the Florida Gulf Coast.* Smithsonian Misc. Coll., vol. 113. 559 pp., illus.

WINTHROP, GEORGE PARKER. 1896. "The Coronado Expedition, 1540–1542." *Ann. Rep. Bur. Amer. Ethnol., 1892–93,* pp. 329–613, illus.

Appendix C

An Act to Establish the "Smithsonian Institution," for the Increase and Diffusion of Knowledge Among Men

[As finally adopted and made into law, August 10, 1846]

James Smithson, esquire, of London, in the Kingdom of Great Britain, having by his last will and testament given the whole of his property to the United States of America, to found at Washington, under the name of the "Smithsonian Institution," an establishment for the increase and diffusion of knowledge among men; and the United States having, by an act of Congress, received said property and accepted said trust; Therefore, for the faithful execution of said trust, according to the will of the liberal and enlightened donor—

Be it enacted by the Senate and House of Representatives of the United States of America in Congress assembled, That the President and Vice-President of the United States, the Secretary of State, the Secretary of the Treasury, the Secretary of War, the Secretary of the Navy, the Postmaster-General, the Attorney-General, the Chief Justice, and the Commissioner of the Patent Office of the United States, and the mayor of the city of Washington, during the time for which they shall hold their respective offices, and such other persons as they may elect honorary members, be, and they are hereby constituted, an "establishment," by the name of the "Smithsonian Institution," for the increase and

248

diffusion of knowledge among men; and by that name shall be known and have perpetual succession, with the powers, limitations, and restrictions, hereinafter contained, and no other.

SEC. 2. *And be it further enacted,* That so much of the property of the said James Smithson as has been received in money, and paid into the treasury of the United States, being the sum of five hundred and fifteen thousand one hundred and sixty-nine dollars, be lent to the United States treasury at six per cent per annum interest, from the first day of September, in the year one thousand eight hundred and thirty-eight, when the same was received into the said treasury; and that so much of the interest as may have accrued on said sum on the first day of July next, which will amount to the sum of two hundred and forty-two thousand one hundred and twenty-nine dollars, or so much thereof as shall by the Board of Regents of the Institution established by this act be deemed necessary, be, and the same is hereby, appropriated for the erection of suitable buildings, and for other current incidental expenses of said Institution; and that six per cent interest on the said trust fund, it being the said amount of five hundred and fifteen thousand one hundred and sixty-nine dollars, received into the United States treasury on the first of September, one thousand eight hundred and thirty-eight, payable, in half-yearly payments, on the first of January and July in each year, be, and the same is hereby, appropriated for the perpetual maintenance and support of said Institution; and all expenditures and appropriations to be made from time to time, to the purposes of the Institution aforesaid, shall be exclusively from the accruing interest, and not from the principal of the said fund. *And be it further enacted,* That all the moneys and stocks which have been, or may hereafter be, received into the treasury of the United States on account of the fund bequeathed by James Smithson, be, and the same hereby are, pledged to refund to the treasury of the United States the sums hereby appropriated.

SEC. 3. *And be it further enacted,* That the business of the said Institution shall be conducted at the city of Washington by a board of regents, by the name of Regents of the "Smithsonian Institution," to be composed of the Vice-President of the United States, the Chief Justice of the United States, and the mayor of the city of

Washington, during the time for which they shall hold their respective offices; three members of the Senate, and three members of the House of Representatives; together with six other persons, other than members of Congress, two of whom shall be members of the National Institute in the city of Washington, and resident in the said city; and the other four thereof shall be inhabitants of States, and no two of them of the same State. And the regents to be selected as aforesaid shall be appointed immediately after the passage of this act—the members of the Senate by the president thereof, the members of the House by the speaker thereof, and the six other persons by joint resolution of the Senate and House of Representatives; and the members of the House, so appointed, shall serve until the fourth Wednesday in December, the second next after the passage of this act; and then, and biennially thereafter, on every alternate fourth Wednesday of December, a like number shall be appointed in the same manner, to serve until the fourth Wednesday in December, the second succeeding their appointment. And the senators so appointed shall serve during the term for which they shall hold, without reelection, their office as senators. And vacancies occasioned by death, resignation, or otherwise, shall be filled as vacancies in committees are filled; and the other six members aforesaid shall serve, two for two years, two for four years, and two for six years; the terms of service, in the first place, to be determined by lot; but, after the first term, then their regular term of service shall be six years; and new elections thereof shall be made by joint resolution of Congress; and vacancies occasioned by death, resignation, or otherwise, may be filled in like manner, by joint resolution of Congress. And the said regents shall meet in the city of Washington, on the first Monday of September next after the passage of this act, and organize by the election of one of their number as chancellor, who shall be the presiding officer of said board of regents, by the name of the Chancellor of the "Smithsonian Institution," and a suitable person as secretary of said institution, who shall also be the secretary of said board of regents; said board shall also elect three of their own body as an executive committee, and said regents shall then fix on the time for the regular meetings of said board; and, on application of any three of the regents to the secretary of the said Institution, it shall be his duty to appoint a special meeting of the board of regents, of which he shall give notice, by letter, to each of the members; and, at any meeting of said board, five shall constitute a quorum to do business. And each member of said board shall be paid his necessary traveling and other actual expenses, in attending meetings of the board, which shall be audited by the executive committee, and recorded by the secretary of said board; but his services as regent shall be gratuitous. And whenever money is required for the payment of the debts or performance of the contracts of the institution, incurred or entered into in conformity with the provisions of this act, or for making the purchases and executing the objects authorized by this act, the board of regents, or the executive committee thereof, may certify to the chancellor and secretary of the board that such sum of money is required, whereupon they shall examine the same, and, if they shall approve thereof, shall certify the same to the proper officer of the treasury for payment. And the said board shall submit to Congress, at each session thereof, a report of the operations, expenditures, and condition, of the institution.

SEC. 4. *And be it further enacted,* That, after the board of regents shall have met and become organized, it shall be their duty forthwith to proceed to select a suitable site for such building as may be necessary for the institution, which ground may be taken and appropriated out of that part of the public ground in the city of Washington lying between the patent office and Seventh Street: *Provided,* The President of the United States, the Secretary of State, the Secretary of the Treasury, the Secretary of War, the Secretary of the Navy, and the Commissioner of the Patent Office, shall consent to the same; but, if the persons last named shall not consent, then such location may be made upon any other of the public grounds within the city of Washington, belonging to the United States, which said regents may select, by and with the consent of the persons herein named; and the said ground, so selected, shall be set out by proper metes and bounds, and a description of the same shall be made, and recorded in a book to be provided for that purpose, and signed by the said regents, or so many of them as may be convened at the time of their said organization; and such record, or a copy thereof, certified by the chancellor and secretary of the board of regents, shall be received in evidence, in all courts, of the extent and boundaries of the lands appropriated to the said institution: and, upon the making of such record, such site and lands shall be deemed and taken to be appropriated, by force of this act, to the said institution.

SEC. 5. *And be it further enacted,* That, so soon as the board of regents shall have selected the said site, they shall cause to be erected a suitable building, of plain and durable materials and structure, without unnecessary ornament, and of sufficient size, and with suitable rooms or halls, for the reception and arrangement, upon a liberal scale, of objects of natural history, including a geological and mineralogical cabinet; also a chemical laboratory, a library, a gallery of art, and the necessary lecture rooms; and the said board shall have authority, by themselves, or by a committee of three of their members, to contract for the completion of such building, upon such plan as may be directed by the board of regents, and shall take sufficient security for the building and finishing the same according to the said plan, and in the time stipulated in such contract; and may so locate said building, if they shall deem it proper, as in appearance to form a wing to the patent office building, and may so connect the same with the present hall of said patent office building, containing the national cabinet of curiosities, as to constitute the said hall, in whole or in part, the deposit for the cabinet of said institution, if they deem it expedient to do so: provided, said building shall be located upon said patent office lot, in the manner aforesaid: *Provided, however,* That the whole expense of the building and enclosures aforesaid shall not exceed the amount of ———, which sum is hereby appropriated, payable out of money in the treasury not otherwise appropriated, together with such sum or sums out the annual interest accruing to the institution, as may, in any year, remain unexpended, after paying the current expenses of the institution. And duplicates of all such contracts as may be made by the said board of regents shall be deposited with the treasurer of the United States; and all claims on any contract made as aforesaid shall be allowed and certified by the board of regents, or the executive committee thereof, as the case may be, and, being signed by the chancellor and secretary of the board, shall be a sufficient voucher for settlement and payment at the treasury of the United States. And the board of regents shall be authorized to employ such persons as they may deem necessary to superintend the erection of the building and fitting up the rooms of the institution. And all laws for the protection of public property in the city of Washington shall apply to, and be in force for, the protection of the lands, buildings, and other property, of said institution. And all moneys recovered by, or accruing to, the institution, shall be paid into the treasury of the United States, to the credit of the Smithsonian bequest, and separately accounted for, as provided in the act approved July first, eighteen hundred and thirty-six, accepting said bequest.

SEC. 6. *And be it further enacted,* That, in proportion as suitable arrangements can be made for their reception, all objects of art and of foreign and curious research, and all objects of natural history, plants, and geological and mineralogical specimens, belonging, or hereafter to belong, to the United States, which may be in the city of Washington, in whosesoever custody the same may be, shall be delivered to such persons as may be authorized by the board of regents to receive them, and shall be arranged in such order, and so classed, as best [to] facilitate the examination and study of them, in the building so as aforesaid to be erected for the institution; and the regents of said institution shall afterwards, as new specimens in natural history, geology, or mineralogy, may be obtained for the museum of the institution by exchanges of duplicate specimens belonging to the institution (which they are hereby authorized to make,) or by donation, which they may receive, or otherwise, cause such new specimens to be also appropriately classed and arranged. And the minerals, books, manuscripts, and other property, of James Smithson, which have been received by the government of the United States, and are now placed in the department of state, shall be removed to said institution, and shall be preserved separate and apart from other property of the institution.

SEC. 7. *And be it further enacted,* That the secretary of the board of regents shall take charge of the building and property of said institution, and shall, under their direction, make a fair and accurate record of all their proceedings, to be preserved in said institution; and the said secretary shall also discharge the duties of librarian and of keeper of the museum, and may, with the consent of the board of regents, employ assistants; and the said officers shall receive for their services such sums as may be allowed by the board of regents, to be paid semi-annually on the first day of January and July; and the said officers shall be removable by the board of regents, whenever, in their judgment, the interests of the institution require any of the said officers to be changed.

SEC. 8. *And be it further enacted,* That the members and honorary members of said institution may hold such stated and special meetings, for the supervision of the affairs of said institution and the advice and instruction of said board of regents, to be called in the manner provided for in the by-laws of said institution, at which the President, and in his absence the Vice-President of the United States shall preside. And the said regents shall make, from the interest of said fund, an appropriation, not exceeding an average of twenty-five thousand dollars annually, for the gradual formation of a library composed of valuable works pertaining to all departments of human knowledge.

SEC. 9. *And be it further enacted,* That of any other moneys which have accrued, or shall hereafter accrue, as interest upon the said Smithsonian fund, not herein appropriated, or not required for the purposes herein provided, the said managers are hereby authorized to make such disposal as they shall deem best suited for the promotion of the purpose of the testator, anything herein contained to the contrary notwithstanding.

SEC. 10. *And be it further enacted,* That the author or proprietor of any book, map, chart, musical composition, print, cut, or engraving, for which a copyright shall be secured under the existing acts of Congress, or those which shall hereafter be enacted respecting copyrights, shall, within three months from the publication of said book, map, chart, musical composition, print, cut, or engraving, deliver, or cause to be delivered, one copy of the same to the librarian of the Smithsonian Institution, and one copy to the librarian of Congress Library, for the use of the said libraries.

SEC. 11. *And be it further enacted,* That there is reserved to Congress the right of altering, amending, adding to, or repealing, any of the provisions of this act: *Provided,* That no contract, or individual right, made or acquired under such provisions, shall be thereby divested or impaired.

Appendix D

Joseph Henry's "Programme of Organization" for the Smithsonian Institution

[Presented in the first annual report of the Secretary and adopted by the Board of Regents, December 13, 1847]

INTRODUCTION

General considerations which should serve as a guide in adopting a Plan of Organization

1. WILL OF SMITHSON. The property is bequeathed to the United States of America, "to found at Washington, under the name of the SMITHSONIAN INSTITUTION, an establishment for the increase and diffusion of knowledge among men."

2. The bequest is for the benefit of mankind. The Government of the United States is merely a trustee to carry out the design of the testator.

3. The Institution is not a national establishment, as is frequently supposed, but the establishment of an individual, and is to bear and perpetuate his name.

4. The objects of the Institution are, 1st, to increase, and 2d, to diffuse knowledge among men.

5. These two objects should not be confounded with one another. The first is to enlarge the existing stock of knowledge by the addition of new truths; and the second, to disseminate knowledge, thus increased, among men.

6. The will makes no restriction in favor of any particular kind of knowledge; hence all branches are entitled to a share of attention.

7. Knowledge can be increased by different methods of facilitating and promoting the discovery of new truths; and can be most extensively diffused among men by means of the press.

8. To effect the greatest amount of good, the organization should be such as to enable the Institution to produce results, in the way of increasing and diffusing knowledge, which cannot be produced either at all or so efficiently by the existing institutions in our country.

9. The organization should also be such as can be adopted provisionally, can be easily reduced to practice, receive modifications, or be abandoned, in whole or in part, without a sacrifice of the funds.

10. In order to compensate, in some measure, for the loss of time occasioned by the delay of eight years in establishing the Institution, a considerable portion of the interest which has accrued should be added to the principal.

11. In proportion to the wide field of knowledge to be cultivated, the funds are small. Economy should therefore be consulted in the construction of the building; and not only the first cost of the edifice should be considered, but also the continual expense of keeping it in repair, and of the support of the establishment necessarily connected with it. There should also be but few individuals permanently supported by the Institution.

12. The plan and dimensions of the building should be determined by the plan of the organization, and not the converse.

13. It should be recollected that mankind in general are to be benefited by the bequest, and that, therefore, all unnecessary expenditure on local objects would be a perversion of the trust.

14. Besides the foregoing considerations, deduced immediately from the will of Smithson, regard must be had to certain requirements of the act of Congress establishing the Institution. These are, a library, a museum, and a gallery of art, with a building on a liberal scale to contain them.

SECTION I

Plan of Organization of the Institution in accordance with the fore-going deductions from the Will of Smithson

TO INCREASE KNOWLEDGE. It is proposed—

1. To stimulate men of talent to make original researches, by offering suitable rewards for memoirs containing new truths; and,

2. To appropriate annually a portion of the income for particular researches, under the direction of suitable persons.

TO DIFFUSE KNOWLEDGE. It is proposed—

1. To publish a series of periodical reports on the progress of the different branches of knowledge; and,

2. To publish occasionally separate treatises on subjects of general interest.

DETAILS OF THE PLAN TO INCREASE KNOWLEDGE

I. *By stimulating researches*

1. Facilities afforded for the production of original memoirs on all branches of knowledge.

2. The memoirs thus obtained to be published in a series of volumes, in a quarto form, and entitled Smithsonian Contributions to Knowledge.

3. No memoir, on subjects of physical science, to be accepted for publication, which does not furnish a positive addition to human knowledge, resting on original research; and all unverified speculations to be rejected.

4. Each memoir presented to the Institution to be submitted for examination to a commission of persons of reputation for learning in the branch to which the memoir pertains; and to be accepted for publication only in case the report of this commission is favorable.

5. The commission to be chosen by the officers of the Institution, and the name of the author, as far as practicable, concealed, unless a favorable decision be made.

6. The volumes of the memoirs to be exchanged for the Trans-

actions of literary and scientific societies, and copies to be given to all the colleges, and principal libraries, in this country. One part of the remaining copies may be offered for sale; and the other carefully preserved, to form complete sets of the work, to supply the demand from new institutions.

7. An abstract, or popular account, of the contents of these memoirs to be given to the public through the annual report of the Regents to Congress.

II. *By appropriating a part of the income, annually, to special objects of research, under the direction of suitable persons*

1. The objects, and the amount appropriated, to be recommended by counsellors of the Institution.

2. Appropriations in different years to different objects; so that in course of time each branch of knowledge may receive a share.

3. The results obtained from these appropriations to be published, with the memoirs before mentioned, in the volumes of the Smithsonian Contributions to Knowledge.

4. Examples of objects for which appropriations may be made.

(1) Systems of extended meteorological observations for solving the problem of American storms.

(2) Explorations in descriptive natural history, and geological, magnetical, and topographical surveys, to collect materials for the formation of a Physical Atlas of the United States.

(3) Solution of experimental problems, such as a new determination of the weight of the earth, of the velocity of electricity, and of light; chemical analyses of soils and plants; collection and publication of scientific facts, accumulated in the offices of government.

(4) Institution of statistical inquiries with reference to physical, moral, and political subjects.

(5) Historical researches, and accurate surveys of places celebrated in American history.

(6). Ethnological researches, particularly with reference to the different races of men in North America; also, explorations and accurate surveys of the mounds and other remains of the ancient people of our country.

DETAILS OF THE PLAN FOR DIFFUSING KNOWLEDGE

I. *By the publication of a series of reports, giving an account of the new discoveries in science, and of the changes made from year to year in all branches of knowledge not strictly professional*

    1. These reports will diffuse a kind of knowledge generally interesting, but which, at present, is inaccessible to the public. Some of the reports may be published annually, others at longer intervals, as the income of the Institution or the changes in the branches of knowledge may indicate.

    2. The reports are to be prepared by collaborators, eminent in the different branches of knowledge.

    3. Each collaborator to be furnished with the journals and publications, domestic and foreign, necessary to the compilation of his report; to be paid a certain sum for his labors, and to be named on the title-page of the report.

    4. The reports to be published in separate parts, so that persons interested in a particular branch can procure the parts relating to it without purchasing the whole.

    5. These reports may be presented to Congress, for partial distribution, the remaining copies to be given to literary and scientific institutions, and sold to individuals for a moderate price.

    The following are some of the subjects which may be embraced in the reports: *

I. PHYSICAL CLASS

    1. Physics, including astronomy, natural philosophy, chemistry, and meteorology.

    2. Natural history, including botany, zoology, geology, &c.

    3. Agriculture.

    4. Application of science to arts.

* This part of the plan has been but partially carried out.

II. MORAL AND POLITICAL CLASS

5. Ethnology, including particular history, comparative philology, antiquities, &c.
6. Statistics and political economy.
7. Mental and moral philosophy.
8. A survey of the political events of the world; penal reform, &c.

III. LITERATURE AND THE FINE ARTS

9. Modern literature.
10. The fine arts, and their application to the useful arts.
11. Bibliography.
12. Obituary notices of distinguished individuals.

II. *By the publication of separate treatises on subjects of general interest*

1. These treatises may occasionally consist of valuable memoirs translated from foreign languages, or of articles prepared under the direction of the Institution, or procured by offering premiums for the best exposition of a given subject.
2. The treatises should, in all cases, be submitted to a commission of competent judges, previous to their publication.
3. As examples of these treatises, expositions may be obtained of the present state of the several branches of knowledge mentioned in the table of reports.

SECTION II

Plan of organization, in accordance with the terms of the resolutions of the Board of Regents providing for the two modes of increasing and diffusing knowledge

1. The act of Congress establishing the Institution contemplated the formation of a library and a museum; and the Board of

Regents, including these objects in the plan of organization, resolved to divide the income * into two equal parts.

2. One part to be appropriated to increase and diffuse knowledge by means of publications and researches, agreeably to the scheme before given. The other part to be appropriated to the formation of a library and a collection of objects of nature and of art.

3. These two plans are not incompatible with one another.

4. To carry out the plan before described, a library will be required, consisting, 1st, of a complete collection of the transactions and proceedings of all the learned societies in the world; 2d, of the more important current periodical publications, and other works necessary in preparing the periodical reports.

5. The Institution should make special collections, particularly of objects to illustrate and verify its own publications.

6. Also, a collection of instruments of research in all branches of experimental science.

7. With reference to the collection of books, other than those mentioned above, catalogues of all the different libraries in the United States should be procured, in order that the valuable books first purchased may be such as are not to be found in the United States.

8. Also, catalogues of memoirs, and of books and other materials, should be collected for rendering the Institution a centre of bibliographical knowledge, whence the student may be directed to any work which he may require.

9. It is believed that the collections in natural history will increase by donation as rapidly as the income of the Institution can make provision for their reception, and, therefore, it will seldom be necessary to purchase articles of this kind.

10. Attempts should be made to procure for the gallery of art, casts of the most celebrated articles of ancient and modern sculpture.

11. The arts may be encouraged by providing a room, free of

---

* The amount of the Smithsonian bequest received into the Treasury of the United States is $515,169.00. Interested on the same to July 1, 1846 (devoted to the erection of the building), $242,129.00. Annual income from the bequest, $30,910.14.

expense, for the exhibition of the objects of the Art-Union and other similar societies.

12. A small appropriation should annually be made for models of antiquities, such as those of the remains of ancient temples, &c.

13. For the present, or until the building is fully completed, besides the Secretary, no permanent assistant will be required, except one, to act as librarian.

14. The Secretary, by the law of Congress, is alone responsible to the Regents. He shall take charge of the building and property, keep a record of proceedings, discharge the duties of librarian and keeper of the museum, and may, with the consent of the Regents, *employ assistants.*

15. The Secretary and his assistants, during the session of Congress, will be required to illustrate new discoveries in science, and to exhibit new objects of art; distinguished individuals should also be invited to give lectures on subjects of general interest.

Bibliography

The literature listed here is confined to three categories: principal works consulted, more or less standard works on the Smithsonian and its branches and leaders, and works that will guide those who may wish to do collateral reading. In addition to the sources listed, special mention should be made of the Smithsonian annual reports, which have recorded in detail Smithsonian activities since the Institution's beginning. Readers will also find very helpful two publications issued in 1946 by the American Association for the Advancement of Science in celebration of the one-hundredth anniversary of the establishment of the Smithsonian: *Scientific Monthly* of November, 1946, and *Science* of August 9, 1946. Both contain a variety of articles by Smithsonian staff members on the history and activities of the Institution. The following list contains several titles, marked with an asterisk (*), that younger readers may find especially readable.

ABBOT, CHARLES GREELEY. *Samuel Pierpont Langley.* Smithsonian Miscellaneous Collections, vol. 92, no. 8. Washington: Smithsonian Institution, 1934.

————. *The 1914 Tests of the Langley "Aerodrome."* Smithsonian Miscellaneous Collections, vol. 92, no. 8. Washington: Smithsonian Institution, 1942.

———— *Adventures in the World of Science.* Washington: Public Affairs Press, 1958.

ADAMS, JOHN QUINCY. *The Great Design: Two Lectures on the Smithson Bequest.* Edited by Wilcomb E. Washburn. Washington: Smithsonian Institution, 1965.

ADLER, CYRUS. *I Have Remembered the Days.* Philadelphia: Jewish Publication Society, 1941.

ALDRICH, JOHN M. "The Division of Insects in the United States National Museum." *Annual Report of the Smithsonian Institution for 1919,* pp. 367–79.

BENNETT, WENDELL CLARK. *The Ethnogeographic Board.* Smithsonian Miscellaneous Collections, vol. 107, no. 1. Washington: Smithsonian Institution, 1947.

CARMICHAEL, LEONARD. *Joseph Henry (1797–1878) and His Smithsonian Institution.* New York: The Newcomen Society in North America, 1956.

*———. "The Smithsonian, Magnet on the Mall." *National Geographic Magazine,* vol. 117 (June, 1960), pp. 796–845.

CARMICHAEL, LEONARD, AND LONG, J. C. *James Smithson and the Smithsonian Story.* New York: G. P. Putnam's Sons, 1965.

COULSON, THOMAS. *Joseph Henry: His Life and Work.* Princeton, N.J.: Princeton University Press, 1950.

DALL, WILLIAM HEALEY. *The Discovery and Exploration of Alaska.* Harriman Alaska Series, vol. 2. New York: Doubleday, Page & Co., 1902.

———. *Spencer Fullerton Baird: A Biography.* Philadelphia: J. B. Lippincott, 1915.

DARRAH, WILLIAM CULP. *Powell of the Colorado.* Princeton, N.J.: Princeton University Press, 1951.

DARTON, NELSON H. "Memorial of Charles Doolittle Walcott." *Bulletin of the Geological Society of America,* vol. 39 (1928), pp. 80–116.

DAVIS, WILLIAM MORRIS. *Biographical Memoir of John Wesley Powell, 1834–1902.* National Academy of Sciences Biographical Memoirs, vol. 8. Washington: National Academy of Sciences, 1915.

DUPREE, A. HUNTER. *Science in the Federal Government.* Cambridge, Mass.: Harvard University Press, Belknap Press, 1957.

*GARBER, PAUL E. *The National Aeronautical Collections.* 9th ed. Washington: Smithsonian Institution, 1956.

GILMORE, CHARLES W. "A History of the Division of Vertebrate Paleontology in the United States National Museum." *Proceedings of the United States National Museum,* vol. 90 (1941), pp. 305–377.

GOODE, GEORGE BROWN. *The Smithsonian Institution, 1846–1896: The History of Its First Half Century.* Washington: Smithsonian Institution, 1897.

——— "The Genesis of the United States National Museum." *Annual Report of the United National Museum for 1897 (1901),* pp. 83–191.

*GURNEY, GENE. *The Smithsonian Institution: A Picture Story of Its Buildings, Exhibits and Activities.* New York: Crown Publishers, 1964.

HAYES, E. NELSON. "The Smithsonian's Satellite-Tracking Program: Its History and Organization." *Annual Report of the Smithsonian Institution for 1961,* pp. 275–322; *for 1963,* pp. 331–57; *for 1964,* pp. 315–50.

————. *Trackers of the Skies*. Cambridge, Mass.: Howard A. Doyle, 1968.

HELLMAN, GEOFFREY T. *The Smithsonian: Octopus on the Mall*. Philadelphia: J. B. Lippincott, 1967.

HERBER, ELMER CHARLES. "Spencer F. Baird: World-Famous Naturalist." In *"John and Mary's College,"* the Boyd Lee Spahr lectures in Americana, 1951–56, Dickinson College. New York: Fleming H. Revell, 1956.

INGLES, LLOYD GLENN. "Barro Colorado—Tropical Island Laboratory." *Annual Report of the Smithsonian Institution for 1953*, pp. 361–66.

JAMES, JAMES ALTON. *The First Scientific Exploration of Russian America and the Purchase of Alaska*. Evanston, Ill.: Northwestern University Press, 1942.

JONES, BESSIE ZABAN. *Lighthouse of the Skies: The Smithsonian's Astrophysical Observatory: Background and History, 1846–1955*. Washington: Smithsonian Institution, 1965.

JUDD, NEIL M. *The Bureau of American Ethnology*. Norman, Okla.: University of Oklahoma Press, 1967.

————. *Men Met Along the Trail*. Norman, Okla.: University of Oklahoma Press, 1968.

KARP, WALTER. *The Smithsonian Institution*. Washington: Smithsonian Institution in association with American Heritage Magazine, 1965.

LANGLEY, SAMUEL P. "James Smithson." In *The Smithsonian Institution, 1846–96: The History of Its First Half Century*, pp. 1–24. Washington, D.C.: Smithsonian Institution, 1897.

————. "The Children's Room at the Smithsonian." *St. Nicholas Magazine*, vol. 28 (1901), pp. 763–64.

LEHMAN, MILTON. *This High Man: The Life of Robert H. Goddard*. New York: Farrar, Straus & Co., 1963.

LENTZ, MARY ELLEN AND PAUL L. "The National Fungus Collection." *BioScience*, vol. 18 (1968), pp. 194–200.

MANN, WILLIAM M. *Wild Animals in and out of the Zoo*. Smithsonian Scientific Series, vol. 6. New York: The Series Publishers, 1930.

MARSH, CARYL. "A Neighborhood Museum That Works." *Museum News*, October, 1968, pp. 11–16.

MORTON, CONRAD V., AND STERN, WILLIAM L. "The United States National Herbarium." *Plant Science Bulletin*, vol. 12, no. 2 (1966), pp. 2–4.

*NEAL, HARRY ELMER. *Treasures by the Millions: The Story of the Smithsonian Institution*. New York: Julian Messner, 1961.

OEHSER, PAUL H. "George Brown Goode (1851–1896)." *Scientific Monthly*, vol. 66 (1948), pp. 195–205.

————. *Sons of Science: The Story of the Smithsonian Institution and Its Leaders*. New York: Henry Schuman, 1949.

————— "The Role of the Smithsonian Institution in Early American Geology." *Journal of the Washington Academy of Sciences,* vol. 49 (1959), pp. 215–19.

—————, ed. *Knowledge Among Men.* Eleven essays on science, culture, and society commemorating the two-hundredth anniversary of the birth of James Smithson. New York: Simon and Schuster, 1966.

OWEN, ROBERT DALE. *Hints on Public Architecture.* Washington: Smithsonian Institution, 1849.

PICKARD, MADGE E. "Government and Science in the United States: Historical Backgrounds." *Journal of the History of Medicine and Allied Sciences,* vol. 1 (1946), pp. 254–89, 446–81.

RATHBUN, RICHARD E. *The National Gallery of Art.* United States National Museum Bulletin 70. Rev. ed. Washington: Smithsonian Institution, 1916.

—————. *The Columbia Institute for the Promotion of Arts and Sciences.* United States National Museum Bulletin 101. Washington: Smithsonian Institution, 1917.

REINGOLD, NATHAN, ed. *Science in Nineteenth Century America.* New York: Hill and Wang, 1964.

RHEES, WILLIAM J., ed. *The Smithsonian Institution: Documents Relating to Its Origin and History, 1835–1899.* 2 vols. Washington: Smithsonian Institution, 1901.

*RIEDMAN, SARAH R. *Trailblazer of American Science: The Life of Joseph Henry.* Chicago: Rand McNally, 1961.

ROBERTS, FRANK H. H., JR. "River Basin Surveys: The First Five Years of the Inter-Agency Archeological and Paleontological Salvage Program." *Annual Report of the Smithsonian Institution for 1951,* pp. 351–83.

—————. "The River Basin Salvage Program: After 15 Years." *Annual Report of the Smithsonian Institution for 1960,* pp. 523–49.

SEARS, PAUL B. *Charles Darwin.* New York: Charles Scribner's Sons, 1950.

SETON, ERNEST THOMPSON. "The National Zoo at Washington: A Study of Its Animals in Relation to Their Natural Environment." *Century Magazine,* vol. 59 (1900), pp. 649–60; vol. 60 (1900), pp. 1–10. Reprinted in *Annual Report of the Smithsonian Institution for 1901.*

SMITHSONIAN INSTITUTION. *A Memorial of George Brown Goode, Together with a Selection of Papers on Museums and on the History of Science in America.* Report of the United States National Museum for 1897, pt. 2. Washington: Smithsonian Institution, 1901.

—————. *Charles Doolittle Walcott, Secretary of the Smithsonian Institution 1907–27.* Smithsonian Miscellaneous Collections, vol. 80, no. 12. Washington: Smithsonian Institution, 1928.

STEGNER, WALLACE. *Beyond the Hundredth Meridian: John Wesley Powell and the Second Opening of the West.* Boston: Houghton Mifflin, 1954.

TERRES, JOHN K. "Smithsonian 'Bird Man' [Alexander Wetmore]." *Audubon Magazine,* vol. 50 (1948), pp. 161–67.

TRUE, WEBSTER PRENTISS. *The Smithsonian Institution.* Smithsonian Scientific Series, vol. 1. New York: The Series Publishers, 1929.

————. *The First Hundred Years of the Smithsonian Institution.* Washington: Smithsonian Institution, 1946.

————. *The Smithsonian: America's Treasure House.* New York: Sheridan House, 1950.

U.S. CONGRESS. *A Memorial of Joseph Henry.* Addresses by Asa Gray, James A. Garfield, William T. Sherman, and others, and biographical memoir by Simon Newcomb. Washington: Government Printing Office, 1880. Published also in Smithsonian Miscellaneous Collections, vol. 21. Washington: Smithsonian Institution, 1880.

*VAETH, J. GORDON. *Langley: Man of Science and Flight.* New York: Ronald Press, 1966.

WALCOTT, CHARLES DOOLITTLE. "Biographical Memoir of Samuel Pierpont Langley, 1834–1906." National Academy of Sciences Biographical Memoirs, vol. 7. Washington: National Academy of Sciences, 1912.

WALLEN, I. EUGENE, FEHLMANN, H. A., AND STOERTZ, CYNTHIA. "The Smithsonian Oceanographic Sorting Center." *Journal of the Washington Academy of Sciences,* vol. 58 (1968), pp. 191–200.

WASHBURN, WILCOMB E. "The Influence of the Smithsonian Institution on Intellectual Life in Mid-Nineteenth-Century Washington." *Records of the Columbia Historical Society 1963–1965,* pp. 96–121.

WESTRATE, J. LEE. *European Military Museums: A Survey of Their Philosophy, Facilities, Programs, and Management.* Washington: Smithsonian Institution, 1961.

WIDDER, ROBERT B. *A Pictorial Treasury of the Smithsonian Institution.* Philadelphia: Chilton Books, 1966.

YOCHELSON, ELLIS L. "Charles Doolittle Walcott, March 31, 1850–February 9, 1927." National Academy of Sciences Biographical Memoirs, vol. 39. New York: Columbia University Press, 1967.

Index